"Let us not forget such a man as Timothy Hackworth. A man who ought to take his place in the history of England, the history of science and the history of civilization. A man to whose intellect, energy and I doubt not faith, the whole race is indebted as the Father of the Locomotive Steam Engine."

Benjamin Gregory
President of the Wesleyan Conference

"Could it be that we've accepted and perpetuated a misleading understanding of what really happened during the pivotal years?

Generations of writers assert that the father and son team of George and Robert Stephenson were the keystone supporting the successful rise of steam locomotive power during the brief cluster of years when its future was less than assured.

Mike Norman's revealing new book looks again at this story from a fresh perspective."

Dave Reynolds,
Director of Shildon Heritage Alliance

"A remarkable piece of writing, evoking the era and the struggle to get Hackworth's legacy acknowledged. It is no exaggeration to say that Mike Norman's book is unputdownable. From page one, you are effortlessly picked up and dropped into the nineteenth century, placing you alongside Timothy Hackworth Young as he meets Major Joseph G Pangborn from the Baltimore & Ohio Railroad Company.

What follows is a quest to reverse the assumption that George Stephenson single-handedly kickstarted the locomotive revolution. In this masterpiece, Norman combines the skills of a virtuoso storyteller with an acute attention to historical detail. All railway enthusiasts should add it to their reading lists."

Jason Ford
News editor, The Engineer

"There can be no argument as to Hackworth's contribution to the story of railways. Sometimes in life the ones who have most skills get on and do the job as only they know how. It was a different world back then. JOB SATISFACTION is their pride and reward. Timothy Hackworth was happy with his place in the world, it would be for others to shout about his skills and this book does that."

Pete Waterman, OBE

"Locomotives, inventions, defeats and triumphs - all along with a cast of real characters including George Stephenson and Timothy Hackworth - are all part of this intriguing, informative and impeccably researched historical narrative. Even without the locomotives it is a fascinating human story."

Pete Thomas, Director
Royal Melbourne Institute of Technology

It Wasn't Rocket Science

A family quest for the truth

Mike Norman

Published by Firstintheworld

firstintheworld.1827@gmail.com / www.timothyhackworth.com

The author and publishers have made all reasonable efforts to contact copyright holders for permission, and apologise for any omissions or errors. Permissions have been given for use:
National Rail Museum – Extensive archive material
Jane Hackworth-Young – Family archive records
OGL v2.0 – Reports of Hansard and Evidence to Commission
Baltimore & Ohio Museum – letter from George Stephenson to Timothy Hackworth

A CIP catalogue record for this book is available from the British Library.

ISBN 978-1-7390819-0-4

Book and cover design by Clare Brayshaw/Mike Norman

Front cover: Based on "Opening of the Stockton and Darlington Railway", painting by Howard Norman. George Stephenson driving 'Locomotion', Timothy Hackworth riding on board as guard, in charge of operations.

Rear cover: Collage of images of the Columbian World's Exposition 1893. Created by Doug Kreuger

Prepared and printed by:

York Publishing Services Ltd
64 Hallfield Road
Layerthorpe
York YO31 7ZQ

Tel: 01904 431213

Website: www.yps-publishing.co.uk

Foreword

Mike Norman has long wanted Timothy Hackworth to get the recognition that he considered Hackworth deserved in the pioneering development of the steam locomotive. Mike realised that a lot more went on than has been recorded, but much of it could be surmised while Hackworth worked on developing each of his inventions. Access to the family archives, combined with extensive digital sources, provided confirming evidence, as did the discovery of a 75-page Foreword that Samuel Holmes prepared for 'Timothy Hackworth & the Locomotive' by his cousin Robert Young.

Samuel lived with his grandfather, Timothy Hackworth, and family from 1847 to Hackworth's death in 1850 and remained in the family home, Soho House, New Shildon a further few years. Samuel saw what was coming out of Soho Works, which inspired him becoming a mechanical engineer before setting up his own business in America.

Mike has taken Samuel's Foreword and extrapolated from it many details that might well have been lost forever. I feel I have contributed a little to this thrilling work as I was the Executor of my uncle Cyril's Hackworth Young's estate and in 2017 found the unpublished Foreword, which had previously been held in America as part of Samuel's estate.

Mike Norman has used his own knowledge of working at the front-edge of technology and, together with new papers that have been found, has compiled an intriguing story. It will appeal not only to the experienced engineer but also to anyone who enjoys a family quest for recognition and social justice.

Jane Hackworth-Young – 2022

Gt, Gt Grand-daughter of Timothy Hackworth

Preface

I can't recall whether it was the small booklet about Timothy Hackworth by T. Greener or the print of the man and his locomotives that got my attention first. Thomas Greener was the son of one of Hackworth's Enginemen, and he had been executor of the estate when Hackworth died. The booklet was the first of a number of attempts to gain recognition for Timothy Hackworth beyond the bounds of Shildon, County Durham. It sought to put the record straight. The print that came down to me was in an oak frame and would have been given to my grandfather, a Methodist lay preacher, when the Chapel in Soho Street was no longer used for worship. The question was what should I, what could I do with my inheritance?

Hackworth's endeavours had been at the cutting edge of the Industrial Revolution and mine had been at the cutting edge of the Information revolution. My experiences of the pioneering stage of our technology mirrored all that I came to consider and learn about their technology – the emergence of the railway locomotive and the power of steam. It became clear there was a story to tell about the early days of the Stockton & Darlington Railway. The picture I had of Hackworth showed him flanked by images of his most famous locomotives – 'Royal George' and 'Sanspareil'. The pamphlet in my possession explained

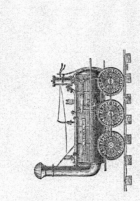

TIMOTHY HACKWORTH'S

"ROYAL GEORGE" LOCOMOTIVE,

Built at New Shildon, Sept., 1827.

The first that exceeded the efficiency of horse power, and the first to which his invention—the Steam blast—was applied.

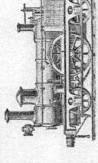

Timothy Hackworth.

Born at Wylam-on-Tyne, Northumberland. December 22nd, 1786; died July 7th, 1850.

TIMOTHY HACKWORTH'S

No. 2 "SANSPAREIL"

(WITH WELDED BOILER, &c.)

SEPTEMBER, 1849.

THE LAST LOCOMOTIVE HE BUILT.

how Timothy Hackworth was the one who proved the case for the Locomotive. It was time to set the record straight.

Correspondence from the Baltimore and Ohio Railroad Company in the Hackworth family archives pointed me to events in America. My researches have uncovered a fresh narrative of a defining time for the Stockton and Darlington Railway, the telling of which fell in with the declared intention of Major Pangborn of the Baltimore and Ohio Railroad Company to honour Hackworth's pioneering accomplishments. The involvement of the family, their engagement with the Chicago World's Fair of 1893 and the subsequent outcome are made a matter of record. How those real events play out over the course of preparations for the World's Fair serves to anchor the story of the quest for recognition for Timothy Hackworth.

Major Pangborn was not without ambition for the exhibits he wanted to create, and he made contact in America with Timothy Hackworth's two grandsons – Samuel Holmes and Timothy Hackworth Young – to enlist their help. Timothy Hackworth Young applies the mind and experience of a locomotive man, as he would have, as he sought to unfold his grandfather's crucial contribution and inventiveness from the records. The story, as seen through his eyes, fulfills Major Pangborn's ambition of having a full account of the locomotive 'Royal George', of Hackworth's invention – the blast pipe – and the significance of his working life.

Those details are true to the facts and Timothy Hackworth stands shoulder to shoulder with first wave pioneer George Stephenson. Conversations between Timothy Young and Major Pangborn are reasonable speculations, bringing them to light, and the glue that would have held events together. Similarly, initial correspondence with Aunt Prudence is assumed to have continued, assisting with the family history, details of which are also true to the facts. Sam Holmes contribution to his cousin's efforts is faithful to the tone of his writing about events, and are in part taken directly from his only recently discovered family records.

The plea in the past from Samuel Holmes about telling the story of Timothy Hackworth had been "Make it readable or your facts will never be learned. It is not the engineering profession we must reach. It is the general public." Based on fresh evidence of letters, notes and handbooks from the family archives, from records of those involved at the time and from reports and science that became more fully understood, this story reaches out, offers new insights and redefines one part of our industrial history. The quest for recognition remains a continuing story.

Michael Alan Norman, York 2022

"people want to receive what's out there in the form of stories, not just facts, opinion, analysis."

Lee Gutkind

"The narrative style, augmented by new research from papers and documents that exist in the USA, creates a real feeling of a personal story, seeking to establish Timothy Hackworth's contribution to the development of the steam locomotive in an accessible way for the 21st Century."

Anthony Coulls, Senior Curator of Rail Transport & Technology, National Railway Museum

The Narrators

Timothy Hackworth Young
Grandson of Timothy Hackworth

Major Joseph Pangborn
Baltimore & Ohio Railroad

Samuel Holmes
Eldest Grandson of Timothy Hackworth

Contents

CHAPTER ONE

Coming to America

Baltimore, Wednesday 16th November 1892

The building on the corner of Baltimore Street and Calvert was not intended to be ignored or overlooked. Five storeys of granite and brickwork were topped by an ornamented mansard roof. Its presence there reflected the substance of the Baltimore and Ohio Railroad itself. It stood out from the crowd. Momentarily a man paused by the building, looking up at the colonnaded battlements of the railway company's head office. Timothy Hackworth Young, to give him the full name by which he had been christened, wondered whether the person who had invited him here could do what he said. Major Joseph G Pangborn had asked him to visit, eager to hear what more could be contributed to honour the inventiveness of a locomotive pioneer. He wondered how much the man really knew of his grandfather, Timothy Hackworth, the engine builder of Shildon. Wondered how this man could do what the Hackworth family, over the years, had found themselves unable.

A letter sent directly from the office of C K Lord, Third Vice President of the Baltimore and Ohio Railroad

Company, was the first contact the Hackworth family had with the railroad company. It had been received by Aunt Prudence in England – aunt Pru as she was known inside the family. Vice President Charles Lord sought the loan of any significant items or material about Timothy Hackworth still in possession of the family. That letter had been followed all too promptly by further correspondence from Major Pangborn, to which his aunt replied with some caution.

However, Timothy Hackworth Young knew that in America, his adopted country, the Baltimore and Ohio Railroad stood head and shoulders above any other in promoting the railway. He had been more than happy to accept an invitation from the 'B&O' to come to Baltimore. This was the 1890s. Railways were big business. Their plan was to put on the biggest railroad exhibition the world had ever seen.

The Columbian Exposition was going to be used to celebrate the birth of the railway, the marvels of the locomotives and the pioneers who overcame formidable challenges to forge a new era of transport. The B&O intended to show the world how this modern magic carpet was unleashed, set free and shaped by truly exceptional men. He was here because they wanted to talk over how they could best make a showing of the work of Timothy Hackworth. Make him, too, stand out from the crowd. That idea stoked his imagination, and he had thrown Aunt Pru's caution to the winds.

He continued to look up at the heights of the building as he briefly tapped his jacket pocket. Major Pangborn's letter of invitation was safely there. Reassured, he dropped his gaze to the building's entrance and back to earth. Timothy Hackworth Young walked into the head office of the Baltimore and Ohio Railroad Company and made himself known, never for a minute realising how significantly it would change the direction of his life. His eyes were about to be opened to the singular accomplishments of his grandfather. Endeavours, too often attributed to the exploits of others who were around him at the time of the Stockton & Darlington Railway, were due to be recast.

* * *

The name on the mahogany door simply said J G PANGBORN. The man who opened it to him was shorter than he expected, had a friendly smile on a well rounded face and sported the neatest moustache he had seen in a long while.

'Timothy, isn't it?'

Timothy looked past the welcome he was proffered and couldn't help staring straight into the space that was Pangborn's office. It was dense with books, with folders, with paperwork. Shelves that went from floor to ceiling were full. The large desk had numerous piles of papers on it. And there was carpet on the floor.

He must have hesitated at the sight. So much so, the man he'd come to see added 'Come in' and, when his visitor did, only then completing his greeting.

'I can hardly believe that we actually have our own railroad man from Hackworth stock here in America. So very pleased you made it.'

Timothy looked around him. Looked at the many photos of Pangborn that adorned the wall of this office; Major

3

Pangborn pictured with dignitaries, Major Pangborn pictured on board trains that bore the distinctive 'B&O' mark of the company, Major Pangborn pictured with the president of the company, Major Pangborn pictured in the construction sheds with newly completed locomotives. He struggled to take it all in. Major Pangborn clearly made up in status for any shortfall he might have in stature.

It was all a far cry from the workaday office Timothy normally shared with other foremen. Men he worked alongside in the locomotive sheds of the railroad company for which he worked in Chicago.

'Do take a chair, sit down. Make yourself comfortable, we want you to feel at home. We have much to talk about.'

He didn't know if he could actually feel at home in these surroundings. This was a far cry from the railroad world that was his lot. His job was to make sure the company locomotives were inspected, always kept up to scratch and, when needed, repaired. Now he had been taken up to the dizzy heights of the management floors of the prestigious Baltimore & Ohio Railroad Company, and in an elevator. If he owned up to how he felt right now, he was more than a touch overwhelmed. He could well believe that an exhibition being organised by someone with this patronage would be something special, and he was here because it was going to include his grandfather. That thought did nothing to clear the heady feeling.

'Well, Timothy Hackworth Young. How does it feel to be part of a family that put the locomotive back on the rails when it nearly fell off?'

Pangborn's words barely registered with him but he knew they needed a response. He struggled to find the right words and could only manage to say, 'I've always been proud of the Hackworth family but when my grandfather had his locomotive works was a long time ago.'

Pangborn carried on talking as he walked his guest to a chair nearby to his desk. 'We watched closely, visited, saw for ourselves what was developing in England. Make no mistake. Your grandfather was one of the pioneers. Making locomotives that worked where others failed. Amongst all the trials and triumphs that it took, I know my work would not be complete without Timothy Hackworth being given his due place.'

He sat down in the grand captain's chair behind his desk, and opened the first of the several folders in front of him. He leant forward, making sure he had Timothy's attention, then set the scene for this encounter.

'Let me explain,' he said in a most convivial tone 'the one thing that is driving us all, and by all I mean the world at large, is the railroad and it's the locomotive that brings it to life. Columbus found this new world of the Americas by pushing forward what his ships could do and where they could go. What better way could there be for us to celebrate the 400 year anniversary than showing the rest of the world our means of travel, our transportation of delight.' He paused. 'You've seen the book – 'On Picturesque B&O' – well we persuaded the committee that the most fitting tribute would be to make 'Transportation' a major focus for the Columbian Exposition. Of course there has to be the showing of the latest wonders from all the countries of the world but Columbus needs a special showing. And who better to do that than the best railroad company in America. Certainly the first...'

Timothy allowed himself a slight grin at that. Every railroad man thought he worked for the 'best railroad company' but this probably wasn't the moment to challenge Major Pangborn.

'Certainly the first...and our Vice-President, Mr Lord, and myself elbowed our way to the top of the queue. Our proposition was that we should have, for the very first time in the world, a section of a World Fair devoted to Transportation. We, that is the directors of Baltimore and Ohio Railroad Company, want to show how we have come to this watershed time in our nation. Not just show off what we now have. We want to tell the story of how others have got us to this moment.'

Pangborn couldn't be said to be lacking in ambition for the company he worked for, and what he said rang true. It also neatly brought together the ambitions of the B&O to set itself foremost in the eyes of all who visited the exposition with the ambitions of a newly settled America, the free and united states of America, to take its place in the world.

Timothy bought it, just as others had. The Columbian Exposition would be a truly historic event. Transportation, railroads, locomotives, all being used as the focus to put down a marker for the United States of America in front of a world-wide audience. He couldn't imagine what that would take, or how it could be done, or how his grandfather's work would fit in.

Major Pangborn had no such shortage of imagination, or plans and facts.

'England was the cradle in which the baby was first laid and nurtured. It took a lot of trial and error. Some folk think that your decisive moment could be traced to the Liverpool and Manchester Railway, to one man – George Stephenson, and to one locomotive – Rocket. We know better.'

* * *

Rainhill, Liverpool, Saturday, October 10, 1829

The crowds in the grandstands, the men of science, businessmen and engineers from around the globe had come for yet another day to witness the most exciting event in the whole year. The Locomotive Trial of the century – finding a locomotive worthy of serving the new railway link between two powerful centres of trade. Today, day four of the trials, George Stephenson, Superintendent of the Liverpool and Manchester Railway, had been watching how 'Novelty', the London locomotive entry, was performing. Saw how well it had made time against the clock. He had become seriously concerned. That was until an official brought him the news. 'It looks like we're going to have to call a halt for today, George. Some repairs need to be done to the loco before they can carry on.'

George Stephenson had seen the reaction of the crowds and realised how eager they were to see the competing locomotives in action. The months of planning for this event had played into the public appetite for a spectacle. Here was a moment to put his competitors in the shade now that technical issues had delayed running the trial of Novelty. This was not an opportunity to be lost. 'Look at the crowds,' he responded. 'You canna turn them away now. We'd best do something.'

He had already completed his own timed runs two days before – comfortably meeting the requirements set by the directors of the Liverpool & Manchester Railway – the L&MR as it became known. He'd met all the conditions. So he ought to; he'd helped set them. He had made sure his son, Robert Stephenson, had enough time to design, build and test the new locomotive; the trial was to be run over a sufficiently short distance that his locomotives would not run out of steam; he'd had a hand in setting the rules – even in the resetting them when the strength of the competition was apparent. Rocket was the entry George Stephenson had made jointly with Henry Booth, the Secretary of the L&MR; joined him as a partner as he'd done in a piecemeal fashion with others before. He had fought long and hard to get to this stage. Even so, the competition was turning out to be stronger than he had expected. Too much was at stake, and it had begun to look too close to call. He had to win. Rainhill was no place for any more setbacks. Time to forget about rules.

George Stephenson grabbed one of the judges' bright green flags. He waved it on high to catch the attention of the crowd who had been waiting all the morning to see Novelty showing its paces. The crowds were still waiting to see something of note. He could give them such a performance that even the few dissenting directors on the L&MR Board would not be able to doubt his supremacy. He was decided, as he told the official in no uncertain terms, 'Let's give them a show – unhitch all the wagons and I'll give Rocket its head. Take off the tender as well. Get down to racing trim.'

The iron horse that was Rocket was pushed up to the starting point, well in sight of the grandstand. George Stephenson stood proudly alongside. His driver in place, Rocket was soon snorting and impatient to show its paces. George Stephenson shouted to the driver, 'They'll see a one today. Give it everything we've got. Get steam up. Don't worry about going high with the pressure. We're not under starter's orders now...'

All eyes in the stand were now drawn to the tall man standing beside the locomotive, waiting on as it got steam up. The bright colours of Rocket had it decked out as well as any of the stagecoaches the locomotive would have to compete with; deliberately casting a lasting impression in the minds of the spectators of the horse drawn stagecoach struggling to match the locomotive. He ought to have had someone blow a blast of 'Tally ho' on a long coach-horn to signal the start. He'd missed a trick there. Shame that John Rastrick, one of the judges and a man who had doubted the wisdom of the decision to use locomotives for the L&MR, wasn't still there to see this run. When he judged the moment right, he stopped waving the green flag, let it drop and shouted to the driver, 'Ha'way man. Let her go and don't slack the reins'.

Rocket with George Stephenson on board flew away. The oohs of astonishment from a thousand spectators told their own story. The speed built up and continued to build as the mile-and-a-half marker approached. The locomotive powered its way forward, faster by far than a team of horses could speed a stagecoach, no matter how fleet of foot they were or how much they were urged on. By his watch, it had taken around three-and-a-half minutes to cover the distance between the marker posts. He reckoned Rocket might have touched 30mph before the driver released steam pressure, more than double the speed it had made under full load in the trial. He'd ask him what pressure he'd let it reach to make that speed – sure in the knowledge that no matter what pressure that turned out to be, it would be below that certified by his son for the locomotive. An exploding boiler, one that would take the life of his driver and sink his ambitions, was a risk to be avoided.

He thought the crowd could be heard applauding, and for them he ran Rocket back and forward over the trial distance again. He'd set the standard, far better than he could have hoped for; better still than it would have been under the scrutiny of the judges. Enough had been done for Rocket to take a rest before any other locomotive took to the rails.

Next time the crowds saw his two main competitors, Novelty and Sanspareil, they would each be hauling a full load of wagons as specified in the trial conditions. After all that the spectators had just seen, no matter how well they performed it would appear they were slower. Much slower. Rocket looked good, performed well and, for the first time for a long while, George Stephenson felt good about the outcome. Today, he had shown Rocket as the most powerful engine in the trials. Any result that put either of the other contenders ahead of Rocket could be challenged – people believed the evidence of their eyes. It was in the bag.

* * *

'...We know better.'

Those words from Major Pangborn registered with Timothy Hackworth Young. They certainly made him sit up and listen. Not much was said within the family about Rainhill. Only that grandfather had taken on too much, was not able to give the competition and his entry as much attention as it had needed. 'Sanspareil', supposedly without equal, had not lived up to its name. He'd been left humbled by the outcome and smarting from the result.

Though Pangborn's words ensured he had Timothy Hackworth Young's full attention, they were nothing as compared to what followed. 'We were as interested as the rest of the railroad companies in the outcome of the battle for supremacy between the locomotive and the established use of fixed steam engines and ropes. Our railroad was underway and we were still keeping to real horse power. Rainhill promised to be a spectacle and a glimpse of the future that no one wanted to miss.'

Timothy knew all about the American railroad companies and their interest in what was happening in England in the early days. There were some among the people he worked with at the Chicago, Milwaukee & St Paul Railroad whose fathers, uncles, cousins had been there at the start of the American experience. Before that, engineers and directors of the Baltimore and Ohio would regularly visit England to keep a check on developments and disasters. The many files he could see on Pangborn's desk testified to that interest. One folder, clearly marked 'Rainhill', lay on top of another marked 'Rocket'. Timothy wondered whether the Major intentionally kept his life similarly well ordered.

Pangborn opened the top folder, flicking through papers, sketches and plans until he came to one report in particular. Timothy waited patiently until Pangborn looked up. When he did, he looked Timothy directly in the eye before he spoke.

'We discovered that John Rastrick, one of the officials, doubted the basis of the Rainhill trial and the value of those results but he had been asked to judge according to the criteria of the directors of the railway – so the award went to the locomotive submitted jointly by their own company secretary, Henry Booth, their own superintendent, George Stephenson, and very conveniently built by Robert Stephenson, his son.'

Timothy started aback, but Pangborn hardly noticed.

'You would have thought the directors would have asked Rastrick to help set the conditions for the trial. He was a respected engineer. They had already called on him to make an independent report on the viability of locomotive power for their railway. That had been prompted when it was heard abroad that the pioneering Stockton & Darlington Railway was thinking of returning to good old dependable horse power. He could have devised a suitable test for the Liverpool & Manchester Railway – a more practical trial, less showboating. He deserved to make more of a contribution than just being a timekeeper and he thought the way the different load to be carried by each locomotive was calculated made no sense.'

Timothy tried to imagine what it must have been like having to grapple with the burgeoning developments in locomotive engineering practice. Science was running well behind, behind a smokescreen of complex formulae and experiments. The Rainhill Trials might have stretched over the best part of a week but what criteria would have been chosen at the time?

Pangborn spoke with the confidence of hindsight. 'Rastrick was right. It didn't prove anything worthwhile. Not like the trial we set to find the best design for our locomotive on our land routes. We took several months performance with real loads for each contestant. Besides which, in design we had to virtually start over. Too many twists and turns on our railroads as they followed the lie of the land. Too easy for your locomotives to leave the tracks – too many disasters. And there was much attention given in England to restricting the radius of curves in your railroad lines...'

Timothy was completely nonplussed by the news about Rastrick. 'But didn't the Rainhill Trials turn out to be a no-contest for Rocket?'

Pangborn had all the details at his finger tips. There were reports aplenty for him to draw on: the newspapers at the time, the journals and a report made by the respected B&O engineer, Winans, on his return to Baltimore.

'Your grandfather's locomotive Sanspareil had a faulty cylinder, blew up and could not complete enough trips running backwards and forwards on the track. The other contender, Novelty, failed at first attempt. Failed again after being repaired. Stephenson and Rocket were left as the only contenders to complete the trial and meet the requirements.'

Pangborn settled back into the arms of his chair. Time for this Hackworth family member to be told the truth.

'Except, Sanspareil had Rocket beaten for speed – and that was with having to haul a heavier load – and the much lighter Novelty looked as though it would have done too. So not much of a trial really.'

He paused for effect.

'The real decider about whether the locomotive was a commercially viable proposition had already taken place with your grandfather's 'Royal George' – now that was a gamechanger and a watershed event.

Pangborn closed the 'Rainhill' folder and, as if to make his point, first slapped it shut with his hand, then he moved it away to one side of his desk.

'And the locomotive that the Liverpool and Manchester Railway opened with was not Rocket but a virtual redesign – which crucially then included one of your grandfather's inventions – and that was what was needed for a version of Rocket to be made powerful enough to operate in the conditions of the actual railroad. The whole Rainhill Trials turned out to be no more than a George Stephenson benefit match.'

Timothy was unsure how to respond to the evident endorsement from this senior figure in the B&O. Very pleasing, but where was this leading him?

Pangborn knew what he wanted of Hackworth's descendant, even if the man himself had no idea. 'In terms of the history of the locomotive, Rainhill was little more than a sideshow and our contribution to the Columbian Exposition is planned to be considerably more than that. We are putting eleven acres of exhibits on display. Our part in the celebration of the whole idea of transportation.... covering the shaping of the locomotive over the years. From the early beginnings right up to the time of the B&O, when we opened the first commercial railroad in America. A most dramatic and historic exhibition. A window into the world of those early pioneers and how what they gave us has become the power that moves the world.'

Timothy Hackworth Young's head was momentarily in a spin. The enormity of the challenge that Pangborn was intending to meet was beyond anything even he as a locomotive man could imagine. Eleven acres of exhibits!

Pangborn's words filtered through those thoughts.

'We'd like you to help us get the Hackworth part of that story right.'

The possibilities for settling the reputation of Timothy Hackworth in such an exhibition, defining his place in the history of the locomotive, was exciting. It was also an overwhelmingly daunting prospect.

* * *

Pangborn had laid out on his desk the working drawings for a locomotive, one that Timothy recognised as being from an earlier age. The boiler was perched on top of two equal sets of wheels. Just two. The pistons were of a simple design and mounted, so far as he could judge, vertically. A far cry from the ones he was familiar with. The sixty ton, ten-wheeled giants that drew the carriages on the railroad between Chicago and St Paul. The ones he serviced, the ones he made sure were kept in good working condition.

'We managed to get all the drawings and engineering notes we needed about the Rainhill contenders. I personally went to England. Met as many people involved as I could. Listened to the stories they had to tell. What had by then become the Science Museum had gathered material that they let me see. All too happy to help. It was only when I saw Rastrick's report and his notebook that I realised there was more to your grandfather than Sanspareil and the Rainhill Trials. Then I was shown the letter from George Stephenson to him and his work took on a new significance for me.'

Pangborn passed a handwritten letter across to Timothy.

'I made a copy and when I showed it to Vice-President Lord we recognised that here was one of the pioneers of the locomotive.'

Timothy very carefully read the letter, paused while he tried to make sense of what Major Pangborn had just said. The letter seemed to be little more than an account of some development work on Stephenson's locomotive at Bolton.

'Timothy, it's not what it says that is so important. It's what George Stephenson doesn't say. He evidently has no comprehension of the significance of the blast-pipe, the device without which locomotives would always have a problem keeping up steam. For some of them, a strong wind was enough to stop them in their tracks. Not enough force. Short of power, even going up an incline. Just like me, sometimes they would run out of puff going uphill, nearly coming to a standstill. These bellows Stephenson talks about, won't do the job. And putting together a locomotive that would meet the requirement of the directors of the Liverpool & Manchester Railway was a serious problem for him.'

It had gradually dawned on Timothy that Major Pangborn was not only serious about making the B&O a tour-de-force in the Columbian Exposition, he wasn't leaving any stone unturned in his pursuit of locomotive history.

'We don't have much material yet about your grandfather and what he did before Rainhill. I'm hoping that the Hackworth family might be able to fill in the gaps in our knowledge.'

Well if that was what was wanted then Timothy knew he could now go to Aunt Pru and explain how determined they were. She would be a fount of wisdom as far as the family history was concerned... and there was cousin Samuel Holmes in New York who had often banged on about Uncle John and what happened in Shildon. He handed the letter back and it was carefully returned to its place in the folder.

'Perhaps,' Major Pangborn said, 'we should talk about that over lunch. I've booked us a table at the Merchants Club.' Pointing to the files and folders that had nearly taken over his desk, he added, 'More relaxing than me fighting my way through all of this lot. And after lunch I'd like to take you up to the workshop at Mount Clare. Let you see what a show we are making ready for the Exposition.'

* * *

Merchants Club, 206 East Redwood Street, Baltimore

The light open and airy dining room of the businessman's club was a place that always ran like clockwork. 'Good morning major,' was the ready greeting from the waiter as he pulled back the chairs from a table by one of the several tall colonnades.

'A menu for my guest please, George. I'll have the clam broth, followed by the lamb with the usual flageolet beans and Lyonnaise potatoes. We'll skip desert today – work to do this afternoon.'

'Yes, Major.'

When the waiter returned, Timothy found himself overwhelmed for the second time in a day. The menu was daunting. It was as good and extensive as any restaurant could have wished for its patrons. Turkey vied with roast ham for his attention, as did filet of sole and sea bass 'fines herbes'. The offerings of terrapin, either Maryland or Baltimore style, and of broiled muskrat, caught his taste buds off balance, and he let his eyes wander back to the more usual fare.

'For you sir? What would you like?'

He went for safe choices. He placed his order for simpler food: pea and tomato soup, followed by the roast ham. That task accomplished, he looked around him.

Beyond their table there was a quiet countenance to everything in this dining room. The waiters were solicitous and almost silently saw to the needs of the club members. Other diners in the room were engaged as much in conversation as settling their lunchtime appetites. This was business as usual, conducted in a place and in a way that was far removed from the hubbub of the lunchtime throngs in more public places.

Pangborn opened their conversation with a rhetorical 'Now where was I?' and then reminded himself.

'Ah, yes. I was telling you about what we found when we went to England. It is difficult now to realise how primitive and faltering was the path to making fully fledged steam locomotives. And it was the North East that had the coal, the black gold of the Industrial Revolution, and the will and need to find a better way than horse power to move it to market. We can't imagine how they struggled to make the technology of steam work, how crude it was and how much people were scared of it.'

Timothy's face showed his surprise. Whether it was the Baltimore and Ohio Railroad or the Chicago, Milwaukee and St Paul Railroad that Timothy worked for, the locomotives they now ran were dependable. The engineering was well understood and keeping the mechanical parts in operation was routine. Difficult for him to imagine a time when it was any other way. So Pangborn painted a picture for him.

'Engines were bitches to drive, bitches to keep repaired. Your grandfather could never have known how much he would depend on his blacksmith skills to keep the show on the road. They rattled and rolled and bits fought against each other till they wore out or fell off or broke. Sometimes it was necessary to take the locomotive apart and rebuild it – the repair shops would be working into the night so as to be ready for the next days work. In the early days worst of all was when they broke down on the line and held up the whole works – horses and locomotives alike, with the drivers left cussing and spitting. Other times it took just a strong headwind and the locomotive was left standing, puffing away to no good purpose. Remember in those days it was possible to run alongside the iron horse – even a brisk walking pace would be enough. That was when your Timothy Hackworth knew something had to be done to move things forward or the company would abandon Stephenson's pet project and leave in tatters his ambition for railways across the whole country.'

Major Pangborn paused, letting his words sink in.

'We heard that horse power was cheaper compared to the locomotives Stephenson was building for the Stockton and Darlington Railway and, the blow that hit home, their share value had halved. It sent shudders through our body of directors I can tell you. Without your grandfather's rock solid experience, ingenuity and observation that could have been an end to it. He'd seen it all. He was the one repairing and making good on the operational difficulties and challenges of those locomotives. What do they say? "Cometh the hour, cometh the man." Well that man was Timothy Hackworth!'

The arrival of the waiter with their first course could not have been more opportune as far as Timothy Young was concerned. He knew about Uncle John and the Soho works in Shildon but not much else had been important to him. Sounded as though Major Pangborn was striking a far too heroic tone, quite at odds with the natural inclination to modesty he'd been told his grandfather possessed.

Pangborn, though had uncovered much more about Timothy Hackworth, and was intent on continuing with the story.

'We visited England – only then was it discovered how much of a pioneer your grandfather was – how his important work was carried out in the most crude and primitive workshops. Which is why in the progression from Puffing Billy at Wylam to Locomotion and then to Royal George, having the enthusiastic support of a powerful local family like the Peases was so important. Stephenson, though, ran so fast and was so taken up with his ambitions that he repaid the support they gave him with a cavalier concern for the debt he owed them and took less care of his son's concerns than you or I would. He would find his place as front-runner was challenged as was his tenacity. And so many vested interests were going to be raised up against the locomotive. Mixing with the big boys, taking them on, he was out of his depth and he and his son Robert would have to fall back on the bedrock of good people – Timothy Hackworth in particular.'

Pangborn stopped when the waiter appeared to clear their plates away, and replace them with the main dishes they each had ordered. Timothy was pleased with his choice and, judging from the smell that came wafting up from his plate, was sure to enjoy the roast ham. He was far less sure about the picture of the Stephensons that was being painted.

'The Pease family, George Stephenson and my grandfather were all of one to make the Stockton and Darlington Railway a success. They were different people, each had their own way and their own contribution to make at the time didn't they?'

'You're probably right. After all, and despite it all, I have some sympathy with George Stephenson. He and I both have a touch of the showman about us, which we use to good effect. There is a lot to be said for capturing the imagination of the world at large; writing about the events we encounter in the world with telling effect, instilling them with an excitement, especially when they are moments of huge consequence. And even more so, when you are fighting against the odds.'

'So what is there about my grandfather that I can help with?'

'What we do not have is a clear account of your grandfather's Royal George locomotive or much more of what he invented between that defining moment and the development of Sanspareil. I checked at the Patent Office in London and, unlike George Stephenson, nothing was filed by your grandfather at the time. There is a story to tell about his work. One I would like to tell at the Columbian Exposition.'

Before Timothy Young could say a thing in response, they were interrupted by the presence, a very definite presence if Pangborn's reaction was any guide, of a person alongside their table.

'This must be your Mr Hackworth's grandson.' A comment that got a smile of acknowledgment from Pangborn and a nod of recognition to the company's Vice President, Mr Lord.

'Don't stop on my account. Trust you are being treated well young Mr Hackworth.'

A comment which needed no reply, and for which he was actually given no time in which to make one.

'You know Pangborn persuaded me. He had collected material, particularly about the 'blast-pipe' and his interview with Morrow to back it up. Left me in no doubt that the reviews after the Stockton and Darlington Jubilee celebrations were well founded – Timothy Hackworth was the father of the locomotive. Do help Pangborn if you can. Always important to give due credit where it's due. As a descendant, and a railway man, you have a duty to ensure his rightful place in locomotive history. Not right, being an unsung hero.'

In the face of being addressed by one of the men who directed the affairs of the Baltimore and Ohio Railroad

Company, Timothy could only splutter, 'I'll do everything in my power you can be sure sir.'

'Knew you'd help. Good man. Off to Mount Clare this afternoon? There is always something very inspiring about a roundhouse – and ours is a beauty to behold. You should see the models of locomotives Pangborn persuaded me to build – and pay for. They already make a stand out display and that's before we mount them in the huge Transportation Building at the exposition next year. They will be the star of the whole expo, won't they Pangborn? It's an important story that the B&O will be bringing to the American public.'

With a cursory wave of his hand towards the two men he strode off, already on his way back to the top floor of the Head Office building content that here was one less thing for him to worry about today.

Timothy looked up as Pangborn returned to their conversation.

'You asked what you could do. Timothy Hackworth has to stand out in this exposition. Stockton and Darlington were the places that gave birth to the railway. He was the one who created a locomotive that was the lynchpin of every other that followed. His "Royal George" saved the day.'

Timothy recalled the phrase which had been used to describe his grandfather, 'Father of the Locomotive.' In the past, so far as he thought about it at all, he had put it down to wishful thinking by family members.

Pangborn though had enough material from records, from people he had sought out, from plans and drawings he had been shown to take a different view and continued,

'He would never have gone backwards from the advances that were made with Royal George. He was adamant Sanspareil was well named – you only have to see the figures for the re-run. Your grandfather kept to his motto, 'simplicity and economy,' as his byword for how to develop the locomotive. And that is where you and the Hackworth family can help us tell the real story.'

Pangborn pushed back on his dining chair, stood up and patted Timothy Hackworth Young on the shoulder. 'Let's get to Mount Clare. You can see what we have made ready so far.'

CHAPTER TWO

Getting drawn in deeper

Mount Clare Roundhouse, that same afternoon.

Timothy needed no urging to follow Major Pangborn. Nothing though prepared him for the sheer size and, yes it has to be said, splendour of what was after all nothing more than a locomotive shed. A huge locomotive shed. The roundhouse at Mount Clare covered more than an acre of ground; the building rose to a height of 125 feet, finishing in a magnificent rotunda. It stood amidst the workshops of the B&O's forty-acre site, and could as easily have been a cathedral as a locomotive repair shop.

The sights and sounds as they both entered the roundhouse told Timothy Young he was on home territory. There is a special sound that resonates at large as huge locomotives are turned, wheeled and are still in steam. Here was a workshop that hid nothing of the work it undertook. And hid nothing of what the B&O were putting together for the Exposition. There seemed to be as many locomotives out on display here as there had been files and folders stacked in Major Pangborn's office. Locomotives as far as the eye could see. Locomotives wherever Timothy looked. Big strong locomotives with their tenders, smaller ones alongside and others that looked back to the very beginnings of locomotives.

'Major, how many locomotives? Are they all going to Chicago for the exposition?'

'We're taking more than thirty modern locomotives and as many again to tell the story of how it was that steam power became mobile and pulled us into a new age of transport. Come on. Let me introduce you to William Tranton. He's another engine man. He'll show us round. Impressed?'

'Difficult to take it all in,' Timothy said. Even more difficult for him to see how the work of his grandfather would stand out against the sheer weight of so many other locomotives. And the site at Chicago that Pangborn was going to use was ten times the size of this roundhouse. Overwhelming.

'What are you showing of my grandfather's work? How can his story be told?'

Major Pangborn made off towards a foreman's office without answer. He opened the door and a man came out to meet the pair of them.

'I'll let William here show you part of the answer. Then we can talk about what more can be done.'

Timothy recognised a fellow locomotive man; a man dressed for work not words.

'William, allow me introduce you to the grandson of Timothy Hackworth. Show him round our work so far. I'll let you tell him our story.'

With a nod of his head, a beckoning hand, the foreman who was to be his guide took Timothy to the start of a line of locomotives.

'Well we start here with one of the first attempts, Blenkinsop's cog wheel drive. And, come round here, there is the Steam Horse, complete with two metal legs to pull it forward. The weirdest contraptions you ever did see were tried, tested...and guess what? Found wanting. Next I'll show you Seguin's multi-tubular boiler locomotive from France...'

Timothy was intrigued at the sights in front of him, went to make a close inspection, cast a workman's eye over what he saw.

'I had no idea. That must have taken some skill to turn some of these to good effect, to beat and hammer a way to making steam locomotive,' he said.

'That was your grandfather's job. Hackworth the engineer,' was the reply. 'Over here his name is on every railway man's lips when you ask them about how it started. It's the byword for engineering. You can always tell a Hackworth-built engine just by its look. And his Albion is still going. So too another of his, Samson.'

They were not names Timothy had heard of before. 'Samson for strength I suppose. Albion, that sounds familiar.'

'Samson and Albion are both locomotives Hackworth sent to work on the other side of the Great Lakes. Unlike others that were built and very soon were scrapped, they kept on working for years.'

'When was that?' Timothy asked.

'Must have been fifty years ago. Around 1840. Then they gave us more than forty years of hauling goods and earning their keep ten times over. And we are getting one of them in working order for Chicago!'

Now Timothy saw how Major Pangborn's life-size models brought into sight the progress of the railways and the progression of the locomotive. He had more than breathed life into events of the past. Then, amongst all that were on display, William had made a point of showing Timothy the three Rainhill contenders. They were there, together: Rocket, Sanspareil and Novelty. Even as replicas, every detail was meticulously on show. Sanspareil stood out with its own message about Timothy Hackworth mounted on a plaque – a definitive statement as to who was the inventor of the crucial blast-pipe.

Pangborn joined them where they stood. He was indeed master of his craft but for this project he wanted to excel.

'Important inventions are what I want to show. We need to give your grandfather credit for all the development and ingenuity he showed, without which we wouldn't be where we are today.'

'How can I help?' Timothy wanted to know. 'What can I add when you seem to have found a way already of making my grandfather stand out from the crowd.'

'I'd like to add a portrait of Timothy Hackworth to the other pioneers in a Grand Inventors Gallery. There must be a photograph or a likeness of him that I could be allowed to have and give to the artist to work from. Some picture that when it is depicted in oils will vividly bring your grandfather to life.'

Timothy Hackworth Young couldn't get the words out quickly enough. He was already indebted enough for how the B&O were portraying his grandfather.

'After all you are doing, I'll move heaven and earth to do you justice. Somewhere in the family there will be exactly what you are looking for.'

Besides showing the world what Hackworth looked like, there was another gap to be bridged. Major Pangborn had rather more planned than Timothy could have anticipated.

'I've gathered material from every source but don't yet have the whole story about Timothy Hackworth. That's where you can help. Mr Samuel Holmes in New York is your cousin, isn't he?'

'Yes he is.'

'And, now that your uncle has died, your cousin will be the one who has the family records. Timothy, I told you we are missing out on a crucial part of the Hackworth story. The part where the locomotive first came of age. The story of what happened at the start and how the railway prospered. You said you were going on to New York with your wife. Can you make time to go and tell him what we are doing? What you have seen. Ask for his help.'

CHAPTER THREE

Visit to a cousin

Wall Street, New York, two days later

New York looked the same to Timothy Young as when he had lived here with his cousin Samuel Holmes. Wall Street looked the same as when he worked here for Sam as a junior shipping agent. The streets were still the same. The office looked the same. Sam looked the same. And Sam was as direct as ever.

'Well, cousin Tim, what brings you on this visit? Family business or railroad business?'

'It's both. It's the upcoming Columbus Exposition in Chicago and the Baltimore and Ohio Railroad Company. We have a chance to help them, and help the family.'

Timothy Young sat himself down in what he had always considered the most comfortable chair in Samuel's office.

'They are very serious about putting the B&O and locomotive centre stage. Can you imagine? The Columbus Exposition. All America will come and visit. The world will come and visit... And their Major Pangborn wants to make a showing of grandfather alongside all the locomotive pioneers. He is serious enough about grandfather and what he did that he wants to add his portrait to what he's calling his 'Gallery of Inventors'.

Samuel Holmes looked at his cousin, and saw the freshness and eagerness on his face.

'So is he to stand next to Rocket and George Stephenson, and do we doff our cap to the master of the railways as we pass by?' Sam sarcastically mimicked the tipping of an imaginary hat as he added, 'Here's to Stephenson, the hustler from the North East of England.'

Timothy ignored the jibe. 'Sam, in the midst of eleven acres of exhibits we have the chance to make grandfather stand out. Let his story speak to hundreds of thousands of people.'

Timothy couldn't get out of his head what Pangborn was intending to do for their grandfather. He would stand shoulder-to-shoulder with George Stephenson.

'They have built a life-size model of Sanspareil, and it has a plaque that says grandfather was the inventor of the blast-pipe. It's too late to have a model of grandfather's Royal George built to add to it. But Major Pangborn – the man organising their part in the expo – is trying to find a model he is told was made of it for exhibition.'

Sam had heard his uncle on the subject of recognition for Timothy Hackworth. He'd heard at first hand nearly twenty years ago all about his fight with the 'great and the good' of the time. When Uncle John had visited he made it clear that one man, Samuel Smiles, had blighted his father's endeavours. Smiles had penned a biography that laid at George Stephenson's feet every achievement of the locomotive, set him on a pedestal, raised him high as the defining example of the self-made and self-improving man of the age. An academic, he knew nothing of the practicalities of engineering or locomotives, but

31

put abroad in his book claims for George Stephenson that overstepped the mark. It sold in its thousands. Samuel Smiles, even when he realised he was wrong, put his own reputation above that of a humble man from Shildon. Not a word about Timothy Hackworth was changed in his book. No credit was given for his inventions. Nothing had changed. Time had not eased any of Uncle John's anger and outrage. Sam had not forgotten.

He was with his uncle so far as any fame and glory accorded Stephenson was concerned. Stephenson was indeed a self-made man. Self-made at the expense of the ideas of others. Whatsoever George Stephenson could lay his hands on he freely made use of for himself. But harsh words in the press and elsewhere had bought no friends to the cause of Timothy Hackworth, even facts failed them in the face of railway mania. Maybe more than fifty years later, the benefit of hindsight and fresh voices might make a difference. His cousin evidently thought so.

'Sam, this is going to be a celebration of all the work that was done to make the locomotive great. I saw and touched more life-size replicas than I could take in. If it was like that for me, who has spent years in the midst of locomotives, the impact on the man who comes to the Chicago Exposition from his everyday life will be enormous. Every visitor will remember the experience for the rest of their life. And they will talk about it – to their friends, their children, their colleagues at work. It is a once in a lifetime opportunity for us.'

Timothy looked for some encouraging response from Samuel, but he seemed oblivious, deep in thought.

'I've told Major Pangborn, one railwayman to another, that I will do everything I can to help him put together all the material we have about grandfather. As favoured grandson, you must have his workbooks, drawings, sketches, letters from his drivers... Any small thing that will bring him and his work to life. Please, Sam.'

Just as when they worked together before, Sam let Tim make the strongest case he could for one of his pet assignments before deciding anything. He weighed this deal up as he would many others. Exposure of the work of their grandfather, in a good light. Exposure to the public at large. To the public in their hundreds of thousands. And the support of the prestigious B&O. This might actually make some amends for Uncle John's failed efforts and to the standing of the Hackworth family.

'Alright Tim, tell your Major to come and see me. I will put it all together.'

There was one thing that Timothy had already committed to for which Samuel held the key.

'Do you have a good likeness of grandfather somewhere. I've told Major Pangborn I'll meet the cost of a portrait for the inventors' gallery – there's one place for a start where grandfather will be seen ahead of George Stephenson.'

Samuel warmed to his cousin's determined start to set the record right.

'Now, you make me feel mean, Tim,' he said. 'If it really is the opportunity you say then I will help with whatever of grandfather's papers I can.' And Samuel knew that he wasn't the only family member who could help. 'Have you thought about contacting Aunt Prudence? Now that Uncle John is no longer with us, she's one person who could tell you about Shildon at the time of Royal George,' was his ready prompt for his cousin. 'And if there ever was a model made of Royal George she would know about it.'

Timothy looked at the familiar smile that was playing across his cousin's face.

'So you will help?'

'Okay. But, remember Tim, talk is cheap. Why don't I write to invite your Major to visit. I'll schmooze him with lunch at Delmonicos. If he's doing everything you say, then I'll join in as best as I can.'

Timothy Hackworth Young left cousin Sam's shipping agency office with considerably less concerns than he had a few hours earlier. He had good news for Major Pangborn. And as it turned out, Major Pangborn would have good news for Timothy Hackworth Young.

CHAPTER FOUR

Letters from an Aunt

In the period that had followed the visit to New York, cousin Samuel Holmes was good to his word, meeting with Major Pangborn and providing extensive details, notes and letters from the family records. Timothy also corresponded with Aunt Pru. He set her mind at rest about the Baltimore and Ohio plans, telling her all about his visit to Baltimore. Reassured, she dutifully responded to his questions and queries.

Nov22/92

My dear nephew Timothy,

I have told everyone about your venture to help get father his rightful place as one of the locomotive pioneers. Who could have imagined it would be in America this would happen? Our father in heaven does indeed move in mysterious ways.

There is so much that can be said. We have tried so hard before that this feels like a godsend. Perhaps Major Pangborn has a copy of the commemorative publication made for the Jubilee celebrations. It is a memoir of Timothy Hackworth that describes his work, the inventions and accords him the title 'Father of Locomotives'. All of which we agree with. Perhaps when you have led a life free from vain boasting you have to have died before you are recognised for what you have done for your fellow men. Our prayers are with you.

With great affection,
Your ever loving Aunt Prudence

Following her prompt, Timothy Young felt suitably encouraged as to spread his net wider. It did not go unnoticed.

Dec1/92

Timothy,
My goodness, how determined you are. I hear you have been in contact with as many members of the family as are alive in pursuit of information for Major Pangborn. I only hope he is as appreciative of your endeavours as we are.

I have now remembered about the work on 'Royal George'. Your cousin Samuel has the workbooks and records of the experiments carried out. Perhaps he has already passed that information to Major Pangborn. Father worked very hard to get that right for the

Peases. They were worried that their whole enterprise would come tumbling down but father was so convinced he knew what needed correcting. Your uncle John told us that father had found a way to improve the heat given by the fire to make more steam than ever before. It proved to be so. Never again did one of our locomotives stand out of breath, puffing away to no good effect. It should have been patented, as John wished for so much of father's work. We would have been better provided and perhaps the Soho works would not have had to be sold.

Here, exactly as Major Pangborn had wanted, was the beginning of the story of 'Royal George'

John was sure that Royal George was powerful enough to meet the needs of the Liverpool and Manchester railway. He always thought that the trial at Rainhill which so vexed father was quite unnecessary. George Stephenson and his sharp practice irked him so.

Give my love to Leonor.

Aunt Pru

He couldn't help but wonder what had happened next. Aunt Prudence would once again put him in the right direction.

Dear nephew Timothy,

Your enquiry has rekindled old memories. Father was in a difficult position. He wanted to show the two engineers, Rastrick and Walker, how capable the locomotive could be and knew that an adapted Royal George would outrun anything the Stephensons would build. The Pease family having set up an engineering works with them, then any entry father made would be in competition with his employer. He did the right thing and sought their permission to enter. Nothing was ever said by them, but we have a sense that the conditions they made did not help. Father was to put completion of all their work first and he was to pay for it all himself. Many nights he worked through into the early hours by the light of candles.

It was a real test. He had to send out to get the boiler built. He had to use Robert Stephenson's works to build the cylinders. That meant he had to share his designs and specifications with them. Fitting it in with the normal workings of the railway was difficult, although the men supported him in what he was doing. And he had no chance to run any trials before he went to Rainhill.

He was reminded of the locomotive he had seen at the Roundhouse when Major Pangborn gave him the grand tour of all that was to be presented at the Exposition. Sanspareil looked well but he recalled the plaque that was placed alongside. Now he understood the handicap his grandfather was working under, and the determination it must have taken. All to little avail on the day.

It was not his finest hour. He beat all others for speed, and would have won but for a failure in the construction. It was something that would have been found and repaired. As it was later. Sanspareil lived up to her name when she performed so well that she was kept in service long after Rocket had ended its days. His design was perfect for the demands of the Liverpool railway.

She went on to say there was more that Hackworth engineering could accomplish

Nothing deterred father, or your uncle John. They swallowed the bitter pill and carried on developing their locomotives. There was some difficulty with the Stephensons later which led John to persuade father to set up on his own. And to patent their inventions.

They designed and constructed locomotives that had power, dependability and durability. One director said 'take them weight for weight, they surpass any other engine on the line.'

Timothy Young though was not. He would seek out yet more information to make the story complete. There evidently were more chapters in the life of his grandfather.

Cousin Sam had told him of locomotives that Uncle John had known of. One's that had left their mark on the international stage. He would go back to what papers Sam had sent throughto Major Pangborn. There was more than 'Royal George' to take into account if he was to do justice to the working life of Timothy Hackworth.'

Dec19/92

Dear nephew Timothy,
How diligent you are. Uncle John would have been full of compliments for you. Father did design the locomotive Samson that you mention. It was for a mining company in Nova Scotia and like all his work, built to outlast the lifespan of its designer. Our time here is so fleeting. Did you see the carriage that father built for the directors of the Baltimore and Ohio company?

Your uncle also went to Russia to deliver a locomotive for the Tsar. He was treated like royalty himself, which he put down to the friendship struck with father when the Tsar visited us. John was only sixteen when he went and it was an exciting trip for him. He told lots of good stories of travels in sledges across the snowy roads. The Tsar was exceptionally pleased with the locomotive, although there were a great number of changes made. A special blessing was given before the first journey.

Do you know when the Exposition will be opening yet? I expect we shall have reports in our papers of the grand event. Enjoy the fruits of your labours and do tell of any especially interesting happenings.

Your loving aunt,
Pru

Unsure what else to contribute, Timothy carefully made copies and summaries of what Aunt Pru had to say about Shildon and her father, forwarding them to Major Pangborn. The fate of the reputation of Timothy Hackworth lay in the hands of the Major and the B&O.

CHAPTER FIVE

Welcome to the Exposition

Chicago, Two months later

Every day on his way to work Timothy Young took to visiting the Exposition site that bordered Lake Michigan, watching as the buildings on Jackson Park took shape. More than a dozen buildings, the walkways and the lakes and fountains were now well under construction. And there was the Midway, with its entertainments and the huge Ferris Wheel that was there to match the accomplishment of the Eiffel Tower at the 1889 Paris Exhibition. Each visit he made left him thinking about how Major Pangborn was going to make use of all that the family had sent him.

He looked at the place where the B&O exhibits were going to be housed and on display. Now known as the Transportation Building, the imposing structure with its long colonnaded façade already stood out. The oversize entrance was still covered in scaffolding but nothing could hide the rich colours that decorated the seven tiers of its archway, colours that stood out from the whiteness of the other buildings. Waiting for its doors to be opened and the world to visit. Eleven acres of locomotives. He couldn't keep from wondering, as he returned to the Western Avenue Roundhouse, when he would get to see the inside.

* * *

Frederick Layton, director of the Chicago, Milwaukee, St Paul Railroad Company – the 'Milwaukee Road' railroad as it was more commonly referred to – had met with his visitors and finalised the details of their proposition. Now he had business to attend to and it concerned one of the company's general foremen. Timothy Young had promptly responded to the request for his presence in the director's office, any touch of his earlier nonchalance dispelled.

'Good morning, Mr Young. I believe you might already be acquainted with these two gentlemen. They have come to Chicago on a mission that we are agreed is in the very best interest of us all.'

Timothy recognised Major Pangborn immediately and then registered that his companion was the man who had encouraged him to help them, Vice-President Lord. What business brought them here? Frederick Layton and his visitors certainly had Timothy's undivided attention.

'As one English-born man to another, I can understand that promoting the cause of English inventiveness in our field would be near to the heart of a man who has made America his home. And for our company, and theirs, we want to put on the best show for the world that we can at the Columbian Exposition.'

Timothy waiting to hear why he had been asked here, listened very carefully to what his director was saying.

'We are going to increase our contribution to what is on display. As a finale to Major Pangborn's historic offering we will place close to it a replica of one of our new style stations, in all it's operating glory. That needs someone I can rely on to give our 'Milwaukee Road' a good showing. Someone with practical railroad experience, but more importantly, with a sense of locomotive history and how we have got to this exciting point in our development.' He paused. 'We are agreed you are the right man for the job.'

At which point Vice-President Lord interjected. 'And you are the right man for us. The one man whose presence will add an authentic historic link to the whole transportation theme. And you'll be able to work with Major Pangborn to ensure events that concerned your family are fully represented.'

Major Pangborn had worked for this moment, and he had played it exactly right. Frederick Layton had had no problem agreeing to the request for his company to stand prominently alongside the B&O Railroad in making a showing in the Transportation Building. Nor a problem in helping a fellow countryman, particularly one who had evidently already made his mark with the B&O.

Frederick Layton continued, 'It will require you to take nearly a year away from operations at the roundhouse, Mr Young. And I have agreed that you need to have seniority appropriate for the job. That needs to reflect on us, and be a mark for others around you of your standing. What do you say?'

Timothy grasped the opportunity, only for a fleeting moment having any concern about the enormity of what he was taking on. 'I'd do anything to be part of this. And if it also means my grandfather and his work can come out of the shadows...'

Pangborn looked toward Frederick Layton and quickly interjected, 'I can't tell you how much it will mean to have a Hackworth on board'. Then, turning to the one man he wanted to help him stage the display of the century, he nodded encouragingly and added, 'We have a story to tell, Mr Hackworth Young.'

Vice President Lord made the moment real.

'Now we have a job to do... Superintendent Young.'

Timothy Hackworth Young, to give him his full Sunday name, was going to be in the front line of making his grandfather stand out from the crowd. Major Pangborn had indeed, in his turn, brought him good news. His voice would be added to those from the family and beyond who had recognised the inventive merit of all that his grandfather touched.

Timothy's eyes would be the ones that saw and brought together the material the Major had so painstakenly accumulated. His eyes would be opened by events from the past, all about the men of the Stockton & Darlington railway and where their endeavours took them. And he would join those left wondering about the Stephensons, father and son. And how they gained advantages for their schemes and ambitions and came out on top.

CHAPTER SIX

Inventors and Inventions

3140, Forest Ave, Chicago Monday March 6, 1893

A letter from England was waiting for him when he got home. He immediately recognised the handwriting. Aunt Prudence would no doubt have been pleased with his news; his appointment as Superintendent of Locomotives for the exposition, and especially about the part he was going to play in honouring the work of Timothy Hackworth.

> *Feb28/93*
>
> *Dear Timothy,*
> *I can hardly take in your wonderful news. It quite excited my day. You must have been looked on from on high. Our Lord has obviously charged you with carrying the torch for your Grandfather - burnishing his reputation with the flame of truth.*

You said in your letter that a portrait of Timothy Hackworth has been commissioned by Major Pangborn to hang in an inventors gallery at the exposition. That will be the first time for a long time that anyone would see your grandfather and George Stephenson stand alongside each other. Side by side in their endeavours to promote the locomotive and the railways. I always knew Timothy Hackworth came before George Stephenson, not only in a school register. Now the whole world will see it too.

I shall write again as soon as I can get my thoughts together. There is a lot that can be put right. I cannot help but think of the words from Matthew's Gospel:.The first shall be last and the last shall be first. Matthew 19:30.

There is so much to say of what we have over the years tried to bring to public attention. Your Uncle John was not always the diplomat in these matters, now this exhibition gives an opportunity to wipe that slate clean. I still can hardly credit that the Baltimore & Ohio Railway Company are being so generous in their support. We have a lot to thank Major Pangborn for.

Your everloving Aunt Prudence

Chicago, Exposition Buildings, Tuesday 14th March 1893

After two weeks, Timothy Hackworth Young had become accustomed to Major Pangborn's enthusiasm. It was infectious. Here was a man pulling together a great sweep of railway history – determined to make a point about the struggles and the wonder of those men who had made it possible and opened up new frontiers. They changed the world forever.

His first day here with him had won him over. Somehow Major Pangborn had a grasp on the detail of the exhibits as comprehensive as any published catalogue. Marshalling the layout and the display of locomotives, old and new, in the exhibition space was well underway. He had it under control. Less so deciding what to do with the hundreds, maybe thousands, of documents, drawings and the like that he had collected. The magpie in him, the reporter's instinct, had gathered all that could be needed to bring the story of the locomotives to life as powerfully as they had brought life and trade to distant parts. The office Timothy had been given to work in was stacked out with paperwork, which of itself was a challenge to a man more accustomed to the practicalities of running a railroad.

Today the portraits of the railway pioneers were going to take their place in the Inventors Gallery. He climbed the stairway to the long gallery and found Joseph Pangborn already there, surveying the fine portraits in oil of five men. Two Englishmen and three Americans. The dignified stance and expression of each man gave little clue to the 'hands on' contribution they had made.

Pangborn waited until Timothy reached a point midway on the gallery, letting him too take in the sight. 'Now, Timothy, what do you think?'

The five portraits dominated the gallery. It was an altogether impressive collection, even while there remained so much clear space around them on the walls.

Having a display of those who had made the locomotive a working possibility was just as important to Pangborn as visitors seeing the 'iron horses' they created. 'We are going to take the visitors back in time, Timothy. Revolution was in the air. Not the French revolution. The revolution of steam power that moved the world. This is about promoting the locomotive, and here in the inventors gallery giving an account that excites the imagination, stirs the emotions.' He pointed to each in turn as he walked with Timothy back along the length of the gallery.

'Here's Mathew Baldwin. He designed 'Old Ironsides' in 1832. It remained in service for over 20 years. His company was for decades the American and the World's largest producer of steam locomotives.'

The next portrait was of a man dressed in a sombre suit, with a halo of white hair and a trim beard to match. He was pictured reposing in a chair, one hand casually to his front the other resting on the arm of the chair.

'Ross Winans was the engineer for my company – Baltimore & Ohio. Inventor of the patented friction wheel and builder of the revolutionary light weight locomotive 'Tom Thumb'.'

Timothy was struck by the imposing form of the third American inventor. His balding hairline took nothing away from the substance of the man and his confident manner.

'Horatio Allen. Chief engineer of the South Carolina Canal and Rail Road Company. At 136 miles it was the longest railway in the world at the time. He was inventor of the swivelling truck for railway cars. And also became president of the American Society of Civil Engineers.'

Pangborn motioned back to the three portraits. 'These were bold and dedicated men – no less determined in what they did than the early overlanders or the Pilgrim Fathers. It was man who had created a mechanical beast that outstripped nature.'

Timothy followed Pangborn as he moved on until they stood in front of the next portrait. 'George Stephenson made sure the world believed he was that man,' he said. 'And Stephenson understood what that meant. He crested the wave of the appetite for the public for travel – for direct contact with the marvel of the technology of the Industrial Revolution.' Then, turning to the portrait of Timothy Hackworth that hung next to him, Pangborn added, 'Power that stood the horse in the shade. Power drawn from metal, wrought by man. Alongside him, your grandfather's works stand the test of time.' He took a moment to remind Timothy, 'Your job is to make sure he too stands out in pride of place among the early pioneers.'

Well aware that his helpmate here had a formidable and daunting task ahead but also that not much encouragement was needed, he added, 'The empty spaces on the gallery wall are our blank canvases to work on. Create an exhibition here that makes clear the challenges your grandfather overcame. The model of Sanspareil and the place of his invention of the blast-pipe are a starting point. Look to my notes, the material I managed to acquire in London and the journals of the engineers. Scour your cousin's documents – they are a treasure trove. Now you can uncover and tell the story of the man who has been called father of the locomotive. And if more space is needed for exhibits we can easily add some display cabinets.'

He faced Timothy Hackworth Young, who was looking up at the kindly features of his grandfather, features that seemed to invite respect. 'Be bold, Timothy. Tell his story well and thousands of visitors to our Transportation Building will remember him long after this glorious exposition has ended.'

Timothy Hackworth Young left Pangborn still admiring the first fruits of his determination to bring to life those who made a success of the railway. He had to admit that walking alongside pictures of those men who had contributed to the birth and growth of the railway was a humbling experience. He, along with the rest of the world, had become accustomed to the dependability, the size and the strength of the modern locomotive. Regular fast services served Chicago to New York. Freight was carried through to Milwaukee. Luxury express passenger services were planned. When these men were working on the locomotive it was little less than a battlefield, ambitious people carving out a new future, changing the face of the world. Proving it could be done. Making good on difficulties, pushing a way through the debris of failures. And his grandfather, Timothy Hackworth, was going to be celebrated here as one of the first.

Timothy had to pass through the other pride and joy of Major Pangborn; the models that had been made of historic locomotives. Buoyed by the prominence already accorded his grandfather, as he made his way back to the more workaday premises of his official office, he sought out his grandfather's locomotive. Standing amidst Stephenson's Rocket and the locomotive Novelty designed by John Braithwaite, Sanspareil was posed in a tableau as one of the main contenders at the all important Rainhill Trials. A trial that settled the future of the famed Liverpool and Manchester Railway.

He went and stood alongside the full-size model of Sanspareil that Pangborn had had constructed. Altogether, despite the evident strength of its construction, it spoke of a time and of the primitive state of engineering. The locomotive's squat boiler rested between its four wheels, the surface of the seams and the slightly bulging rear plate were punctuated with the rivets that held back the pressure of the steam. The wheels came up to his chest. He stood back to see the top of the cylinders that reached high above the boiler, and the chimney that stretched even further upwards. Two big upright cylinders drove down directly onto the rear wheels, and their motion was passed to those in front by a metal bar that joined them together. The chimney was secured to the body of the cylinder by a single sturdy stay, and within that lay the contrivance that gave it its power – the restricted orifice of the steam blast-pipe.

When he had visited Sam Holmes in New York, Sam had shown him the letter from Baltimore and Ohio that encouraged him so much. Charles Lord, the vice president of the B&O Company, was quite definite in his opinion of Timothy Hackworth. He had written 'There is no question in my mind as regards him being the inventor of the Blast Pipe'.

He looked down to the inscription on the plaque that lay at the foot of the locomotive and read the words; words that suggested all did not go well for Sanspareil at the Rainhill Trials –

"The engine had only commenced running when one of the cylinders cracked through the bore into the steam port extending along its side, the thickness of the metal having been reduced there by imperfect moulding and boring, to hardly more than a sixteenth of an inch. Its final breakdown upon the course was not attributable to any defect in principle of the engine, and it was very highly thought of by many of those competent to judge."

Major Pangborn had been right. Seemingly, all did not go well for his grandfather on that day at Rainhill, Liverpool. How he had fared, and how George Stephenson fared would be at the heart of the story. He drew his foreman's pencil and carefully recorded in his notebook all the words of the inscription. Here was the starting point for him to uncover the part his grandfather had played in those momentous times when the locomotive first drew breath.

* * *

Timothy heard the sharp footsteps of Major Pangborn approaching along the corridor even before he heard the door to the office being opened. He had with him one of the porters, who was laden with a near mountain sized collection of bound papers in their stiff covers.

'Right Brigham, put those down next to the boxes on the table over here. Mr Hackworth Young, its time to make a start.'

Timothy turned in his chair to see what had been brought in, just as Brigham was equally speedily sent on his way.

'Thank you,' he heard Pangborn say to him. Then, checking his pocket watch, he added, 'Meet me at the entrance to the Transportation Building in half an hour, Brigham. We have some more exhibits to check in.'

Timothy pushed back on his chair, stood up and went towards the table set in the corner of the room. He mused and stroked his beard as he inspected this latest offering from the man he was to work alongside.

'I've brought you some of the engineering journals. Far less inclined to take the side of one party or favour another. I probably shouldn't say it, but they are more reliable than the reports from the newspapers. And everything that your cousin sent to us is in these boxes.'

There had been no time to see what Sam Holmes had thought fit to provide, but Timothy knew his cousin would have already made sure that all he had sent was relevant to the task in hand – making good on his grandfather's reputation and standing. And Pangborn had yet to make his own contribution.

'Look on the shelves above your desk... copies of official reports, files with details of locomotives from round the world.' Pangborn paused and a smile crept across his face. 'I can't believe how generous people have been... altogether thousands of documents.'

Timothy understood and believed the generosity. New world, new possibilities. An opportunity to break loose from the chains that bound the past. 'Well, if they are anything like us then they will be so pleased that their works or those of relatives and family might be brought into the light of day.'

As was often the case with Major Joseph Pangborn there was more he had to say. 'I also have had sent through my copies of published works, ones that now, with the benefit of hindsight, add a commentary alongside what was done. You may want to take what you can from 'The life of George Stephenson' by Samuel Smiles, and from the work of Zerah Colburn. He was an accomplished engineer well before he started writing about locomotives.' Pangborn looked at the table, judging that sufficient space remained clear. 'There is also a copy of Wood's Treatise on the Locomotive.' He was one of the very early practitioners – got some basic things completely right, and then some he got just as wrong. There are also notes I made directly from some of the official records.'

Pangborn might not have had time himself to follow the story of Timothy Hackworth from start to finish but he was sure he knew where to suggest to look for the answers. 'All told, more than enough for me to do justice to the Stephenson contribution'. He steered his helpmate in what he thought was the right direction, 'And for you too.'

Timothy Hackworth Young had a sense of direction, well at least a starting point prompted by the plaque that stood with his grandfather's locomotive. 'I stopped by Sanspareil. Those first locomotives are quite a sight. Our visitors should be thrilled to see so many of them together. To get to where we are today from there...' He took out his notebook and read. 'As Hedley was the first to make a practical demonstration with the avowed purpose of showing the adhesion of smooth wheels to smooth rails, so Hackworth was the first to determine the blast-pipe as essential.'

Pangborn listened patiently while words he had written for the plaque, the one that stood in front of Sanspareil, were spoken out loud. 'The Royal George was a six-wheel engine, the Sanspareil, a four-wheel engine. The exhaust steam taken from the cylinders was sent into a single contracted nozzle, or blast-pipe, turned upward in the centre of the chimney...'. Timothy purposefully laid his notebook on the table, alongside all that Pangborn had brought. 'So to get to grips with my grandfather's invention I have to look further back. Back to Royal George.'

'Royal George?' Pangborn reflected for a moment. 'Built by Timothy Hackworth for the Stockton and Darlington Railway in 1827. It should have stood first in line. That was the one that got away from me...'

Timothy posed the question that had begun to trouble him. 'And Rainhill? Doesn't everybody in England say that 1829 was the major turning point for the locomotive?'

'It was. Then Rocket faced direct competition from the two other designs of the locomotive. Sanspareil and Novelty. All very excitable times. Of the three, Novelty seems to have captured the imagination of all who saw her. Favourite of the thousands of spectators. All very different to anything else. A copper cylinder at one end and all the water and fuel she needed was already on board at the other end. No separate tender. A real lightweight. She sprinted away at speed.'

'But it was the Stephensons, father and son, who were responsible for the locomotive that was "last man standing".'

'Yes. Competitors didn't actually make a worthwhile difference in the end. Rocket prevailed. George Stephenson's remarks when he saw Novelty for the first time was that she had no guts. We never really found out then...'

Timothy didn't need to hear much more. He realised he was about to delve back into those pioneering times. Apply his own technical knowledge to bring the work of his grandfather firmly into the light of day, on show at one of the largest exhibitions that the world had seen. Looking around at all that surrounded him, he interrupted, 'There will be reports in here of all this won't there? '

Major Joseph Gladding Pangborn beamed. Timothy Hackworth Young was about to make the start he had hoped for. He had judged him well.

CHAPTER SEVEN

Blast pipe story

Same day

The first question posed by Timothy Hackworth Young came out of the blue so far as Pangborn was concerned. It was a long time since he had raised the arguments and the evidence that brought Charles Lord on side.

'How come you were persuaded my grandfather was the inventor who deserved credit for the blast-pipe? I was always told it was Timothy Hackworth who devised that most important invention. We all believed that...'

'And everyone else laid claim to it, Mr Hackworth Young,' were Pangborn's words of caution.

The Hackworth that was part of the locomotive man in Timothy Young was never far from the surface. 'I understand how it made the locomotive what it is today. A blast of steam that drew air through the coals and made it burn bright and strong. And we are very particular about where it is sited in the chimney. That didn't come about by accident, no matter what anyone says.'

Major Pangborn had seen more than enough evidence of the competing claims when he left America and went in search of the history of the locomotive. Some claims were based around the models he had made, and they remained fresh in his mind. 'Many early locomotive builders wanted the credit. Trevithick's family claimed he had it. Truth is he noticed that as the steam went through the chimney that the coals shone brighter. But left it at that. Observation without any action. Even Gurney, with his steam carriages for the roads, claimed he had shown Hackworth how it was done. Most of all it was claimed to have originated at the coal mine at Killingworth, under the direction of Nicholas Wood its manager, and built into his locomotives by one George Stephenson.'

'Killingworth?' queried Timothy. 'That was years before Sanspareil took to the rails at the Rainhill Trials.'

'And years after, by the time of the Anniversary of the Stockton and Darlington Railway, all hell had still been let loose. A satirical magazine had a field day with a cartoon that caricatured all the contenders, furiously backstabbing and fighting each other. That image lodged in the mind.'

Timothy was at a loss. 'How did it get settled then? We, the family, claim it for Timothy Hackworth. No locomotive could do its work without it.'

Pangborn pointed him in the right direction. 'Along came a worthy academic – Samuel Smiles. He had seen the virtue in the self-made man. The Industrial Revolution had turned things on their head. Science, the supposed mainstay of all that was to be known or regarded, had become the tortoise in the race against the rampant running of the hare of progress. It was down to individuals to forge the way forward by the light of their own endeavours. He made it his work to tell the stories of the lives of those men who did that. He made heroes of all those he portrayed as giants of their time.' He pointed toward the table with its weight of books. 'His book about

George Stephenson ran to five editions in the first year it was published. Not just thousands, but tens of thousands of copies of were sold, and his words were taken and given credence as much as the words on the tablets of stone Moses brought down from the top of the mountain.'

Timothy still waited an answer. 'What was his settled determination about the blast-pipe? Who did he award the crown to?'

'Well, no surprise,' Pangborn replied. 'He claimed it for George Stephenson. His heroic self-made man; the self-educated man; the determined man who overcame all ahead of him – the man who was defined by the railways he initiated and built.'

'Now you do have to tell me what changed your mind? Was it something you saw in Timothy Hackworth's locomotives? Or something that happened at the Stockton and Darlington Railway?'

'I like to think I have done a thorough job of getting the facts together – done a reporter's job on the fascinating history of the locomotive. I don't have the benefit of an engineer's training or sufficient knowledge of locomotives to rely on my own judgment. After the heat of putting the railways in place had died down, Zerah Colborn took on that task. He had seen the developments and practice in England, and in America. He published and edited journals about locomotives and he had a degree of technical competence and recognition that would stand up...'

'You talked with him? He persuaded you?' interjected Timothy, becoming increasingly impatient.

'No... He didn't. One of your grandfather's drivers did. He had written that George Stephenson had ridden with

Timothy Hackworth on Sanspareil and asked him what gave the locomotive its power. Hackworth had explained the nature of the pipe work in the chimney. And that meant from whatever source Stephenson acquired the know-how about the blast-pipe, he did not know about it at the time of Rainhill. And Timothy Hackworth definitely did.'

The practical side of Timothy thought he saw an end in sight. 'So that was it then. You set it right and the rest of the world took note?'

'Not yet. There are millions who still believe otherwise. It's less than 20 years ago that Timothy Hackworth was written out of the official Golden Jubilee celebrations of the fifty years of the Stockton and Darlington Railway. A commemorative statue for Edward Pease, the Quaker founder of the railway, was unveiled. His name and that of George Stephenson were prominent on the archway into the celebration lunch. The name Hackworth never appeared.'

The puzzlement reappeared on Timothy Young's face, and he gave his beard another smoothing brush with his hand as those words sank in.

'As Smiles, that author of Stephenson's aggrandisement said, "The battle of life is, in most cases, fought up-hill; and to win it without a struggle were perhaps to win it without honour." This will definitely be to your family's honour, Mr Hackworth Young.' He put on his most affable smile of encouragement, 'Blast pipe, Rainhill and the Royal George are part of the Timothy Hackworth story. You are going to have to seek out the evidence for the public at large to see and be persuaded.'

Pangborn walked over to the door and left to find Brigham and Go about his other duties.

* * *

Timothy Young found the book he wanted among the pile that Brigham had set onto the table. The title, Life of George Stephenson, appeared above the single word of the author's name, Smiles, on the spine. It was a moment's work to release it from the stack of books and journals, and he had it to his hand. He looked at the tooled and decorated cover of the book, a gold embossed image of a locomotive standing out in the centre. Rocket he assumed. Timothy walked back to the surety of his desk, set the book by Samuel Smiles down in the centre of his desk and set himself in place in his chair.

Looking inside he was faced with a woodcut picture of the sombre features, receding wavy hair and decidedly bushy eyebrows of the man who had carved out railways worldwide. He turned the first few pages, until he came to the list of contents. A man's life and the times captured apparently in two parts, in twenty three chapters and, his heart sank, through several hundred pages. But there it was, amongst the detail spelled out for each chapter was the reference he needed to find: 'Invention of the Steam-blast.'

Below the title of Chapter Five, the sections were each described: The Locomotive Engine – George Stephenson Begins Its Improvement. And the final sections described as 'George Stephenson's Study of the Subject – His first locomotive constructed – His improvement of the Engine, as described by his son – Invention of the Steam-blast.' That phrase caught his eye; 'as described by his son.'

When he turned to those pages he was impressed with the lack of ambiguity as to the pronouncements. George Stephenson had invented the 'steam blast' for his locomotives at Killingworth, forty years earlier.

> *"my father, having observed the great velocity with which the waste-steam escaped, compared with the velocity with which the smoke issued from the chimney of the same engine, thought that by conveying the eduction steam into the chimney, and there allowing it to escape in a vertical direction, its velocity would be imparted to the smoke from the engine, or to the ascending current of air in the chimney. The experiment was no sooner made than the power of the engine became more than doubled; combustion was stimulated, as it were, by a blast ; consequently, the power of the boiler for generating steam was increased, and, in the same proportion, the useful duty of the engine was augmented."*

Robert Stephenson must have possessed a prodigious memory or had extensive drawings and notebooks of his father to lay such a claim. There was more. "I can not pass over this last-named invention of my father's without remarking how slightly, as an original idea, it has been appreciated; and yet how small would be the comparative value of the locomotive engine of the present day without the application of that important invention." He lifted his head momentarily. Appreciated... Slightly appreciated... The blast-pipe was and is, he thought, what gets the locomotive under sufficient steam. He read on, "it is necessary to observe that the next great improvement in the same direction, the 'multi-tubular boiler,' which took place some years later, could never have been used without the help of that simple expedient, the steam-blast..."

Well, looking at what took place at Rainhill when the multi-tubular boiler first appeared would tell the truth of it... Apparently Stephenson was being credited with having already recognized the blast-pipe as crucial. The letter that Major Pangborn had referred to told a different story. He cast his eyes to the end of the section and the chapter. What words could yet be added to all these faulty recollections?

> *"It was only when the improved passenger engine, fitted with the multi-tubular boiler, was required to be run at high speeds that the full merits of the blast were brought out; and in detecting its essential uses in this respect, and sharpening it for the purpose of increasing its action, the sagacity of Timothy Hackworth, of Darlington, is entitled to due recognition."*

* * *

He read the words again, unable to believe what was written. His grandfather damned with faint praise... That wasn't either professional or friendly. It was, though, a way of holding on to George Stephenson's reputation at Timothy Hackworth's expense. And no one was there to gainsay it. Robert Stephenson might have been President of the Institute of Civil Engineers when this was written, already had honours showered on him for his works and been an elected MP, but that was no way to treat Timothy Hackworth – or the truth – with any respect.

* * *

Chicago, Exposition Buildings, Wednesday 15th March

He had slept on his disquiet and brought it with him to work the next day, refusing to let it go. Instead he sought his way through some of the engineering journals that Major Pangborn had brought to the office. He found Timothy Hackworth had not, as far as the blast-pipe was concerned, been given credit for even "detecting its essential uses" or "sharpening it for the purpose of increasing its action". He also discovered little was said about " the sagacity of Timothy Hackworth, of Darlington"; nothing that could count as receiving " due recognition." In fact little was written about the blast-pipe at all until after the Rainhill trial.

NEW YORK AND PACIFIC STEAMSHIP, COAL
AND LUMBER COMPANY.

DIRECT STEAMSHIP LINE
BETWEEN
NEW YORK AND PACIFIC COAST.
MONTHLY SAILINGS.

MORRIS BUILDING,
64, 66 & 68 BROAD STREET.

SAMUEL HOLMES, General Agent.
Cable Address: Holmes, New York.
Watkins & Scott's 10th Edition Codes.
Telephone Call: 1010 Broad.

NEW YORK, 18th March 1893

Dear Timothy,

Now you can see what Uncle John was up against. Smiles broadcast the untruths about the Stephensons and the world believed him. The truth is there for you to find and include as part of the display you make for grandfather.

Your Major Pangborn told me he had a copy of the letter from George Stephenson to Timothy Hackworth that confirmed he knew nothing about the 'blast pipe'. I also sent over a copy I had taken in case he had mislaid his own.

No matter what anyone else has said, the notebooks from the Soho works at Shildon have the detail of various trials and experiments that grandfather carried out. When he was building 'Royal George' was when he perfected the 'blast pipe', keeping his keen smith's eye on how hot he could raise the coals and how much extra water it turned to steam. How else would 'Royal George' have satisfied the Board of the Stockton and Darlington Railway? Remember they didn't think it could be done.

Should that not be enough to carry the day and the argument, then look to the letter his driver Morrow sent to the 'Engineer'. He is quite emphatic.

Uncle John had much to say about the claims of other people. He dismissed them all, and there was no-one contradicting him. He had always wanted grandfather to register his inventions, but that was only to happen at the end of Timothy Hackworth's working life. The 'blast pipe' is an essential part of the locomotive. No one has registered a patent. They couldn't because they could never show they were the first to use it. And, mark well, the Stephensons were quite aware of patent law and the 'blast pipe' was never specified as part of the early patents they registered. The person who brought it forth into the light of day, who perfected its use and gave the benefit to the world was our grandfather.

Make the truth stand out against the deceits.

SH

Thus prompted he would look to what material Sam had provided.

Chicago, Exposition Buildings, Monday 20th March

Major Pangborn had been right. Sam Holmes material was a virtual treasure chest of correspondence, papers, plans, and notebooks. The letters were bundled all together: letters between Timothy Hackworth and George Stephenson, letters from Edward Pease, correspondence with Robert Stephenson, communications with John Rastrick and James Walker, both eminent engineers. Meticulous as ever, Sam had put the letters in date order. The one he was looking for was from George Stephenson, written after the events of 1827 at the Stockton and Darlington Railway but before the momentous Rainhill Trials.

He found it, dated 28 July 1828. George Stephenson was involved with a new locomotive. Originally being built for working on the construction of the Liverpool and Manchester Railway, removing the spoil from the cuttings and tunnels, it was instead designated for the Bolton Railway. In the letter he described the way he had found of providing sufficient power for the heavy duty work to be undertaken.

Addressed to Dear Timothy, it read:

> We have tried the new locomotive engine at Bolton, which works beautifully; there is not the least bit of noise about it. We have also tried the blast to it for burning coke, and I believe it will answer. There are two bellows worked by eccentrics, underneath the tender. The line will be opened on 1st August. It is too far for you to

come, or I should be glad to see you. Write me about the engines by return of post if you can.
Yours truly
Geo Stephenson

Those first words were a reminder of the preoccupation of holding down the noise created by early locomotives as the exhausted steam 'trumpeted' its way through the chimney. Those that followed gave the lie to any early use by George Stephenson of the blast-pipe as the means to provide a forceful supply of air to excite the coals. His solution, instead, was to use not one but a pair of bellows. Timothy Young recalled the conversation he had with Major Pangborn about this letter when they first met, and how much store he had set by it. He now understood how the claims of Smiles, the author of the biography of George Stephenson, could be resisted. Not only did George Stephenson, one year before the test of the locomotives at Rainhill, not employ a blast-pipe, he clearly had no inkling as to how essential it was for any locomotive. Whatever ideas had come about at Killingworth couldn't match up to it, and evidently didn't lead on.

Perhaps Major Pangborn had more to say about the invention of the blast-pipe. Maybe there was evidence to uncover about when it did become part of the Stephenson's story of the building of the locomotive. He had to work on more than that to do justice to Timothy Hackworth. He had to find the markers for when his grandfather brought the blast-pipe to the locomotive. A good starting point might be when the railway was struggling to survive; when Timothy Hackworth had to step in and build Royal George.

CHAPTER EIGHT

In at the Start...

Chicago, Exposition Buildings, Wednesday 22nd March

Another day at the office thought Timothy Young as he sat at his desk and looked over the schedule of locomotive arrivals at the Transportation Building. His job today would be to meet up with the porters, the signallers and the movers at the rail lines that brought exhibits up to the rear of the massive nine-acre annex with its two-and-a-half miles of track. All told the plans showed there were more than one hundred locomotives already in place, not counting the Baltimore and Ohio replicas, and a further final five arriving this afternoon. He'd check their stands and make sure they were in the correct position, properly identified with sufficient information for the public to appreciate their place in the history of the locomotive.

'Some fresh air, I think don't you'. The arrival of Major Pangborn suggested a welcome diversion from checking schedules. He put his hand on Timothy Hackworth Young's shoulder. 'I'm struggling to see how we can do justice to all the diagrams, plans and other artefacts that I'd managed to accumulate. Thought that we might get some inspiration from how the Arts Building has managed their collections. They must have something of the same dilemma. How to fit it all in.' Major Pangborn looked over at the paperwork on the desk. 'Come on, Superintendent, let's hit the trail.'

Little further encouragement was required and the two men made their way outside. A few steps took them away from the front of the Administration building and towards the main station with its access to the Intramural Railway that, set twenty five feet above the ground, ran around the site of the exposition. Along its continuous three-mile track passengers were afforded views of the various buildings and the lagoon as they were transported from site to site in the open sided carriages.

Ticketed, both men took their place on the bench seats of a carriage. 'There we are Mr Young, yet another form of transportation. Electric power drives this little beauty. We couldn't let steam locomotives completely dominate everything.'

The Intramural Railway rose above the Annex of the Transportation Building, giving Timothy Young a clear view to his right towards the central lagoon with the Wooded Island beyond. Major Pangborn pointed out the places where even more alternative forms of transport would be available to the visitors; the moorings for the waterborne electric-powered launches and the gondolas, with their human power, as well as the piers for the lakeside steamers. As they approached the station for the Midway Plaisance, he saw to his left the Ferris Wheel and the vista of the more than fifty entertainments gathered from around the world that stretched down the length of the one-mile-broadwalk. Major Pangborn prompted him to look to his right again, to the main steamer pier bringing in visitors from across Lake Michigan.

'If you look towards the lake you can see a sight that must have been made for visitors from England. Next to the pier where hundreds of people will alight from the steamers is our battleship 'Illinois', and opposite it, on the other side of the pier, one of the typical Tudor buildings brought to life here. The first thing visitors will see is a celebration of your country, ahead of the buildings for Russia, Germany, France and the rest of Europe. Even ahead of our State Buildings. I'll take my hat off to whoever pulled that one off for you.'

The last stretch of their ride took them past the grandiose building created to honour the State of Illinois, in a magnificent setting set in front of their destination; the Arts Building. Timothy Young had become accustomed by now to the scale of the exposition which he was sure would go down in history as having eclipsed all previous International Fairs, but even he stood back in admiration at the sight. Major Pangborn took it in his stride as they walked their way down the tree-lined promenade from the station at 57th Street in full sight of the buildings representing each of the states of the newly established United States of America.

'America on display,' he said. 'Do you know, when it came to the inauguration ceremony last October, each state had to march in the parade in order of when they acceded to the Union. That was a telling of our history all on its own. Now they vie with each other to tell their own story, and they all do it in some style. You really ought to see what they have done.'

Timothy looked at the sheer variety of the buildings he could see, all differing in shape, in size and in height. Opposite the Fine Art Building, a replica of the Liberty

Bell housed in its high tower that topped the building told everyone who passed by that this was Pennsylvania setting out its stall. Beyond it was the contribution from New York. An imposing frontage ran for over two hundred feet, three times the length of its neighbour, and the building stood four storeys high. The size and ostentatious decorations dwarfed all others around; ornamented balustrades ran the length of it, a colonnaded semicircular part that graced the side, the wide portico entrance, including busts of the state governors, surmounted by a gigantic replica of the great seal of state, decorative plasterwork above reaching to a further floor and above that a roof garden watched over by two square towers.

'New York catches the eye, doesn't it,' said Pangborn, as he paused on his way up the wide stairs that led to the west entrance to the Fine Arts building and looked back. 'They're just trying to make up for losing out to Chicago in the competition to hold this World's Fair, the Columbian Exposition to celebrate the discovery of America. It took seven secret ballots before we passed the bar, and they were behind us in every vote. Judging by the size of the building for the state of Illinois and its setting on the lakeside, Chicago is looking to keep it that way still.' He turned, walked beyond the pair of lions that guarded the stairway, passed through the twelve foot high colonnades, above which befittingly stood six life-size classic statues, and through the entrance into the Fine Arts building. In front of him was all the evidence that was needed.

The spirit of the Fine Arts looked overwhelmed by their exhibits. Busts, sculptures and bronzes filled the floor space. White sculptures in finest Italian marble stood in groups on solid black stands. Small busts lined the edge of the numerous alcoves. A series of clay models, including a group of bull fighters with their capes and swords in various poses, had come from Spain. Major Pangborn was stopped in his tracks, looking around for some respite from the visual onslaught. He beckoned to Timothy and together they approached, then entered, one of the alcoves. His eagle eye had spied a display of plans and drawings, looking very much like the sort that he wished to have displayed for the locomotives in their Transportation section.

'Now I wouldn't have thought of displaying them like this,' he said. 'They have set up huge panels, put them slightly offset and used both sides. You get so much more than displaying these drawings on the wall.' He looked critically at one display which had ten architectural drawings of plans for rooms in a large house on one side of the panel, and on the other were displayed four large sets of plans – one for a church, another for the façade of an Oxford college, one for a new school and a final one for the bell tower of a cathedral in Dalmatia. 'I think we might have the answer here as to how to handle those hundreds of plans and drawings that I have acquired.'

Timothy Young was more interested in the paintings that he found in the alcoves further on. There were magnificent paintings from private collections; images from the eyes of Monet, Pissaro, Renoir, Manet and Tissot all touched his heart. Major Pangborn had his eyes elsewhere. Looking above to the upper gallery, he saw the same layout of displays was used there. 'This is much like our display space... Let's see what they have done here,' was said as he walked over to the staircase that led up to the gallery on the next floor.

Arraigned in front of him he found a multitude of displays that mixed engravings with lithographs, pen and ink drawings with wash drawings, prints with black and white oil pictures. None were overwhelmed by others. Even the mixture of sizes of the artefacts on a single display detracted not at all from any one of them. Drawings of an open-air theatre in Provence sat comfortably alongside a sketched portrait, sat next to a picture titled 'Preparing for the final dance'. More than a dozen pieces by the same artist were mounted on one side of the display, and on the other four large drawings depicting in turn a veiled Moorish woman, one titled 'The Iroquois Arrow', followed by two portraits. Those who had responsibility for finding a way of offering visitors to the exposition the host of artefacts acquired by the Fine Art Department had solved Major Pangborn's problem for him. The task he and Timothy Hackworth Young now had to take on was adapting the material for the Transportation Building so it displayed in a similar way. The detour this morning had been well worthwhile. Timothy Young was less convinced. He was still left with other more immediate and practical issues to deal with today.

'We can make such a display alongside the historic locomotives as will fully inform visitors, and we can bring the works of our inventors truly to life with displays alongside their portraits,' was said with palpable enthusiasm. 'You can breathe life into your grandfather's work. Alongside I will set out the accomplishments of George Stephenson. Stockton and Darlington Railway will meet the Liverpool and Manchester Railway. We can tell the story of two Titans.'

Superintendent Timothy Hackworth Young for a moment felt the full weight of his responsibilities, including that of his middle name. He stood erect as he surveyed what had been accomplished here and saw in his mind's eye the beckoning blank spaces on which he could record the life of the inventor of the blast-pipe. Major Pangborn's enthusiasm opened the door to the works of Timothy Hackworth being seen in as favourable a light as possible. What had to be said about his grandfather could now certainly amount to more than the short description currently attached to his locomotive Sanspareil.

* * *

On the return journey Timothy Young made the mistake of asking Major Pangborn what he thought he might want to cover of the life of George Stephenson. Ambitious enthusiasm meant that once started it proved difficult to stop him. Timothy had forgotten that the Major had made it his job to visit anywhere in Europe where there was news of locomotives. He had met and visited everywhere worthwhile, and he had used his reporter's instinct to grasp the points of interest and impact in a story. The time on the Intramural Railway sped by as they returned to the Transportation Building.

'George Stephenson was a man of his times, as they say. Samuel Smiles had reason to hold him up as the man who had taken it upon himself to see to his own improvement.'

Pangborn continued, 'Times were changing. England was at war with France only a hundred years ago. We had seized our independence as well. And then we fought you again. That was little more than ten years before the locomotive got under way. Revolution and reformation were in the air. So too was the Industrial Revolution, literally. Steam, and the power it brought, changed what man could accomplish.'

Pangborn paused to take a breath and bring himself back on track. 'No longer was a man destined to follow in the steps of others. Those were shackles that George Stephenson found he could cast off. New skills were being developed, new horizons and new opportunities were opening up.'

'I thought that possibility came to every one. Nothing special about George Stephenson because of that,' was Timothy's rejoinder. 'Cousins Sam Holmes and Robert Young both prove it. Sam saw America as his new horizon, took on the challenge of the steamship business. Robert went to Malaya founding his own engineering company in the Straits Settlement. Took on the task of editor and chairman of the Penang Gazette, and, if that wasn't enough of a new skill, played a part in the running of the Settlement. All new skills, new horizons. And my decision to come to America, to play my part here in a different sort of railway business, does too.'

'George Stephenson, though, had no formal education. Not a setback you had to endure. Even as a child he worked. His had been a harsh life in every way. And he came through trying family circumstances. His wife died, his father died, he went away to work, he turned his hand to any thing that put coppers in the purse and food on the table.' Pangborn looked directly at Timothy, 'Above all he was inquisitive about how things worked. That saw him progress. Ralph Dodds, manager at the time of the Killingworth mine – or viewer as the job was referred to then – was at his wits end. The stationary pump wasn't clearing the water that flooded into the mine. George Stephenson had worked out why. From the moment he rebuilt it, made it work and saved the pit, his life changed. He took on the mantle of experimental engineer.'

'Was that when he invented the 'Geordie' lamp?'

'That's a different story. No place for it here but it says a lot about George Stephenson and the times. He might not have been at the coal-face but he had a keen view of the hazards of explosions and fires from the gas that could build up underground. He invented, experimented, refined and had built a miner's lamp to detect explosive gas. Locally it was named after him. Only a scientist, part of the Royal Society, had built one too, and that carried his name. There was a real hoo-ha about it all. Science was supposedly pre-eminent. Respected and respectable. Stephenson found himself on the wrong side of the establishment, publicly vilified and personally abused. Described as uncouth and uneducated. We would say, "Born the wrong side of the tracks".'

Timothy Young had a question. 'Was it his to claim then?' The same question that was posed almost every time the locomotive was the subject of discussion.

'Eventually, after lengthy acrimonious public debate, honours were divided. Science, and its adherents, were unaccustomed to their rule being opposed. They were the custodians of the laws that governed the world and the knowledge of it – but not any longer.' Pangborn was on his reporter's soapbox. 'They had marked the card of the wrong man. Locomotives were on the way and inventiveness not science was what was called for. George Stephenson made sure the establishment felt that.'

The two men alighted at the Intramural Station placed conveniently for them right at the Transportation Building, intent on killings two birds with one stone; Timothy Young to ready things for the arrival of the locomotives, Major Pangborn to assess the placing of display material alongside and around the Baltimore and Ohio exhibits.

They headed directly for the middle aisles of the annex, finding the examples of early locomotives standing impressively in line, waiting to tell their unique and historic story.

Pangborn walked down the line, counting them off. 'York, Mercury, Tom Thumb'. They both stopped by the last one, a diminutive locomotive. 'That's barely big enough to be called a locomotive,' commented Timothy Young. 'An unlikely stripling of a youngster when you see it next to some of the hardened monsters it took on. Might have been the first in America...'

Pangborn couldn't resist, 'It showed us for the first time that, when it comes to delivering power from steam, size isn't everything.' And, as he walked them past the trio of contenders in the trial that had decided the future of the Liverpool and Manchester Railway, he added, 'Much like the Novelty that competed for the prize at Rainhill, about which George Stephenson was less than complimentary.'

Next in line came the Rastrick's 'Stourbridge Lion', Seguin's locomotive and Stephenson's 'Blucher'. Timothy Young had more interest in one of the early American locomotives, the first passenger locomotive of the Mohawk and Hudson Railroad Company of New York, visible behind those. It was set in front of the contribution from the Pullman Company, with its display of comfort and ostentation. The contrast was not to be ignored. 'What must people have thought when they saw this old locomotive with its passenger carriages. They were no more than the old bone rattling stage coaches put on wheels. They were the same. Same length, same height even down to the roof rack for luggage and outside passengers, same bright colours.'

'Only faster...,' was the swift comment at his shoulder. 'You think that surprising, wait till visitors see Blenkinsop's locomotive with its wheels running along a toothed track, and Trevithick's single piston locomotive that has so many cogwheels it looks as though it could have been built in a clock factory. No matter how wild the ideas looked, from hereon the locomotive was on its way. The owners and managers of the coalmines in the North of England were the ones who took up the challenges, and our two heroes, George Stephenson and Timothy Hackworth, pulled it off.'

The manager at Killingworth mine was Nicholas Wood and he saw the work with George Stephenson develop until the locomotive 'Blucher' was the result. A workable locomotive that was thought worth taking out a patent for.

Timothy Young's attention was taken by the next exhibit in Pangborn's looking back in history. 'What is this odd-looking carriage doing here among the locomotives? They might be primitive but this has no cylinder or boiler that I can see.'

Major Pangborn explained. 'The other mine was Wylam, owned by Christopher Blackett. William Hedley was the overseer, the "viewer" as he was called, and what that trolley established was his contribution. Not much to look at you think? It was crucial.'

Just as crucial for Superintendent Timothy Young was seeing, in return for his time spent at the exposition, what had been done to benefit the development of the railroad company for which he worked. They had been promised they would be put in an advantageous position compared to their competitors. Other railways had, just as Major Pangborn predicted, concentrated on showing off at the Columbian Exposition the biggest and the best that they had to offer. The Major had a different take on all this. He had a view. The exhibit of historic locomotives had been planned to create a different sort of impression. Through what they had done to celebrate one hundred years of America, not what they had on offer, visitors would see the Baltimore and Ohio line as the foremost in America. Long after they left the Columbian Exposition, every time they reflected on the experience, they would think above all of the B&O's historic celebration of the locomotive. It would make them stand out amongst the bewildering mass of their competitors. In the same way he suggested that the Chicago, Milwaukee and St Paul Railroad could gain more advantage and in a different way to their competitors. Pennsylvania Railroad had decided to mount a veritable museum piece to show off their latest and best offerings; a complete station, tracks and locomotive. Instead, Major Pangborn had suggested, they could understate the benefit of travelling on the Milwaukee Road Railroad by showing just one innovative piece, the comfort of their premier carriage with seats styled as easy chairs, and lighting. What was missing was some way of capitalising on the thousands of visitors who would be swept along on a wave of enthusiasm for locomotive travel. 'What better way to build on that than having a full-size booking office, providing information about routes and timetables and selling tickets?' Major Pangborn had asked. 'It could be sited in the body of the main hall, catching the attention of visitors as they entered and again as they left the Transportation Building enthused with the idea of locomotives, railroads and travel'. That idea was a keenly tuned commercial proposition and instantly found favour. Between them the Major and the Superintendent had sufficient influence and status to bring it about.

The Chicago News when told of the venture, duly reported the establishment of the Chicago, Milwaukee and St Paul innovation with exactly the right level of enthusiasm and adulation :-

> "a model union ticket office in the building and with it a bureau of information. George H Heafford of the Chicago, Milwaukee and St Paul originated the idea and has carried its plans to completion. Visitors will be able to get any information they want about any subject at the office. They can buy tickets for and learn exactly when the first train starts, as well as connections they can make."

Timothy Young on his way out of the building would certainly inspect and make sure all was up to standard in that exhibit, perhaps less an exhibit of a railway booking office than a commercial venture about which his company could be proud. First, he had to spend some time in the Transportation Building Annex, marshalling the staff and the plans for the arrival of the Canadian Pacific train with its complement of carriages. That too was a striking exhibit of modern locomotive prowess that had to be put in place and on show. By comparison, he was left with a feeling that the role of Wylam, the coal mine where his grandfather first worked, was being underplayed in the exhibits about the early history of the locomotive, despite what Major Pangborn had said. He needed to hear more about George Stephenson and Timothy Hackworth in the early days.

* * *

Back in the office, Timothy was still thinking about how in the early days the locomotive had progressed from the time of Trevithick and Blenkinsop. The odd device he had seen near the start of Pangborn's historic display was a puzzle. It wasn't capable of going anywhere.

'What was the purpose of the trolley you have put in the display? You said it was built by Hedley, the viewer at Wylam.'

'It was a massive step forward. Hedley was the one who thought that there was no need for all the clever thinking that looked at cogs, and racks, and chains, to give the locomotive a hold on the track. Instead, something to push against so the effort of the piston and a flywheel alone would move the locomotive contraption forward. He thought that the weight of the locomotive on its own would bear down and there would be sufficient friction force to stop the wheels spinning and for the locomotive to push against.' Pangborn paused. 'Before everyone else, and without any science to rely on, he was right. Changed the way that tracks, wheels and locomotive were brought together. The experiments with his "Test Carriage", that trolley, trying it with different weighted loads, pushed by some brawny men, gave him all the information he needed. The locomotive could be set free, to run on its wheels unencumbered. That discovery was crucial to all that followed.'

Timothy Young sat back into his chair, watching and waiting for the Major to reach out for some report that might offer more detail. There was no need, Major Pangborn had all the detail he needed firmly in his mind.

'They had all fumbled, that was until George Stephenson settled on a combination that worked, and an approach that worked for him too. The single cylinder and the flywheel it had needed were ditched, the drive was conveyed to the pairs of wheels by a cog wheel, it hauled a heavier load than a team of horses could manage. It worked. And he found other work as well.'

Pangborn mused at the fruit that Killingworth had borne for Stephenson. After Killingworth he had an established reputation and was sought out as the one man of experience of railways. The Major continued, offering Timothy Young a glimpse into how Stephenson pushed on towards the high ground of his career. 'The Hetton railway was the next step, this time a line of eight miles from pit to wharf on the River Wear. He surveyed the line. Well his brother did that for him. By then he had got the problem of the railway track itself sorted – an improved rail developed with Newcastle-based iron founder William Losh. He had a locomotive design that did the job – that was protected by the patent with Ralph Dodds, the mine manager. So he turned his attention to using locomotive and stationary steam power instead of horses. In the space of two years he built five locomotives for Hetton, employing chain-coupled wheels as a development of the original Killingworth locomotive.' Pangborn paused, here was the start of the way of making progress that seemed to define George Stephenson's life. 'He had the confidence of the mine owners at Hetton. They were persuaded about what Stephenson could do, had belief in the man and had the money to fund his project. George Stephenson managed to keep any number of balls in the air at the same time. All the while he was being paid for working at Hetton, he also retained his job at Killingworth and his pay from there.'

Timothy Young realised that such events would quite naturally, for Major Pangborn, form a starting point for his account of the life of George Stephenson. Details he would set in a display alongside the portrait in the Inventor's Gallery. He made a mental note to discover what had happened with his grandfather at Wylam at that same time. Pangborn continued, 'Then Stephenson did it again. The Stockton and Darlington Railway was another step up. This was to be a new 26-mile railway to compete with the canals. Nicholas Wood, the manager from Killingworth, helped him persuade the Quakers from Darlington to take him on. He had become the man who could show that he had done it all – who could build a railway to move the goods from the coal mine to the ships, and build the locomotives that would power it.'

Major Pangborn moved to where his files and documents had been placed. He took hold of one, marked in a bold, firm, hand 'STOCKTON AND DARLINGTON RAILWAY', while he continued to tell the story. 'And Edward Pease, the driving force and the commercial mind behind the scheme, was taken with the man and what he was shown – the actual evidence on the ground of Stephenson's locomotives, the way the man desported himself and the vision he had, and would hold to, of what the railways could become.'

He brought out and showed Timothy how bold a step George Stephenson had taken. How he alone had changed the face of what a railway was projected to become. He found the note he had made about the Stockton and Darlington Railway, put it on the desk and read aloud from it. 'May the 23rd 1823. That was a defining moment. The wording of the Bill that went to Parliament was revised specifically, and for the first time, to include the possibility of locomotive transport – and a railway that would be defined by the epithet "private risk for public good" was set in motion. Stephenson's eye was also on the future – his and that of the locomotive.'

Pangborn stood back while he let the significance sank in. 'Stephenson had done it again. He had a willing patron. He did it again – initially keeping to the job at Killingworth, and being paid for managing the survey and construction of the Stockton and Darlington Railway. If there was private risk it was not going to be his risk.'

Timothy Young nodded an acknowledgement. He had noted from the version of history that Samuel Smile's book offered, that George Stephenson had not so much assumed any risk as persuaded Pease and his Quaker colleagues to take on even more than the railway alone. Quite separate to the surveying and building of the Stockton and Darlington Railway, he persuaded Pease and others to invest in a locomotive manufactury – a separate firm to make his patented locomotives for all and sundry.

Where Watt had made his fortune from stationary steam engines, George Stephenson evidently had his eye on the locomotive business. No one else in England had that vision, or the experience to bring to bear on each and every railway that was built. 1825 was the year when it happened for George Stephenson. On every account that Timothy Young had seen, Stockton and Darlington Railway opened to a fanfare and the astonishment of all.

Pangborn continued, 'The iron horse was the final nail in the coffin of what had been 'Old England'.... the horse as the means and measure of transport was going to be supplanted, and the canal system was about to be drained of its trade.'

Timothy Young had listened as the advancement of George Stephenson was told. He felt compelled to raise some sort of query. 'Major, didn't Timothy Hackworth figure in this at all?'

'I don't know,' was the honest reply. 'There was the Wylam mine as well as that at Killingworth, but nothing much was developed there. It's Wood's work and Stephenson's accomplishments we know about at this stage of railway development. And that was going to lead straight on past the Stockton and Darlington enterprise to the grandest scheme of all, the Liverpool and Manchester Railway.'

Any railway man, thought Timothy Young, would realise that Pease would have had as much interest as George Stephenson in seeing the manufactury prosper beyond meeting the requirements of the Stockton and Darlington Railway. No surprise he was happy to endorse George Stephenson in his appointment as engineer to that line. It was an ambitious undertaking, but George Stephenson was driving on to make his mark with the longest railway yet between two of the largest cities and their international trade. The good times were going to roll... for George Stephenson, for the Board of the Liverpool and Manchester Railway, and for Pease and his partners in the manufacture of locomotives.

Like the accomplishments of Columbus that the exposition was celebrating, George Stephenson had a definite view in sight. Railways would stretch across the country to the benefit of all. He would be determined to press on regardless with that end in mind, and be tested to the limit and beyond. From what he knew already, Timothy Young believed none of that could have proved to be plain sailing. He also recognised the task ahead of him to match his grandfather's accomplishments with those of George Stephenson.

'Major, if I'm to do justice to my grandfather I'm obviously, as you did, going to have to look back as far as Wylam, before I can look forward to Sanspareil and the Rainhill Trials.'

CHAPTER NINE

Letters from afar....

Chicago, Exposition Buildings, Thursday 30th March

A brisk walk to the exposition site in the fresh weather of the end of the month lifted Timothy Young's spirits. There were four more weeks to go to the grand opening and, with Major Pangborn's connections and support, most of the organising work had been finished. People had been allowed to visit the Exposition at half price as it all took shape, and their numbers were increasing with the days that went by.

What a vista was on display. As far as the eye could see, buildings had risen from the flatland that had been Jackson Park. A multitude of different shapes dominated the view, each designer working hard to make their contribution stand out or to reach higher still than its neighbours. And what displays there must be going to be housed within those buildings.

Time now, though, to get a grasp of the information that would be put on display for his grandfather. It always seemed that Major Pangborn had a definite idea of the story he intended to tell about George Stephenson, as he did with so much about the history of the locomotive.

Timothy had reached out to the family to fill in the gaps he had so far as Timothy Hackworth was concerned and had not been disappointed. Both Aunt Prudence and his cousin Sam had written back, although as always Sam Holmes took him to task.

March26/93

My dear nephew,

How well you seem to be progressing. Of course we must tell the story of Wylam, which is where all your grandfather's works started. He took on the task of foreman smith. The same as his father before him. The skill was only passed on in that way. He served his full seven years as apprentice at Wylam, and gained as strong a reputation for his works as his father had. He understood making things in metal far better than most others, which is when he became part of the push by the owner to make a railway to transport the coal from the mine. He played a major part in building the Test Carriage that showed plain rails could be used, and in the engineering of the first locomotives : Puffing Billy, the Wylam Dillies and, before them, the Grasshopper type of locomotive. The Wylam Dillies were the great success - and he made sure they went on forever, and so it seems they did for more than forty years.

Christopher Blackett the owner and William Hedley the viewer weren't the only ones to take an interest in what he did. George Stephenson was forever coming by to see what your grandfather had made. Father said we shouldn't be surprised that Stephenson's first successful locomotive was half from Wylam and half from Blenkinsop at Leeds.

Your grandfather thought his life at Wylam, like the operation of the mine, was settled until in 1816 events took a different turn. Things changed when Blackett went to London and left Hedley in sole charge. How it happened that he left Wylam, your grandfather never said, but Hedley was prepared to put Mammon before God. He wanted the mine worked every single day of the week. Timothy Hackworth would never work on a Sunday.

Our family were always dedicated Methodists, drinking deep from the font of both Timothy and his wife Jane. Once you come to Jesus, which your grandfather had done in 1812, you put your life in His hands. There is no other way. Sunday, the Sabbath, was the Lord's day. Not a day of work. He had the Lord's work to do, preaching the gospel as the disciples had and bringing people to Jesus. His principles would not allow him to work on a Sunday. It was obviously God's will that he moved elsewhere.

Your grandfather was offered the job of foreman smith at Walbottle mine by William Patter who managed and had part ownership of it. There he remained for 8 years, accomplished in his metal working, happy with his growing family and his preaching. It was only the departure of George Stephenson's son, Robert, for South America that changed things. Timothy Hackworth was taken on as a borrowed man - a hired hand - to run the locomotive manufacture in his stead. Which is how he came to be associated with the Stockton and Darlington Railway. He did such a good job that George Stephenson tried everything he knew to keep him,

In the end that is what happened. Timothy Hackworth took on responsibility for the locomotives, the stationary engines, the line and it's working. The rest of the history you will find is well recorded, more than sufficient for your needs and by engineers better able than me to provide the details.

Write to me about anything more you think I can help you with.

Your loving Aunt

And her letter had been followed by a lengthy reply from cousin Samuel Holmes in New York.

NEW YORK AND PACIFIC STEAMSHIP, COAL AND LUMBER COMPANY.

DIRECT STEAMSHIP LINE
BETWEEN
NEW YORK AND PACIFIC COAST.
MONTHLY SAILINGS.

SAMUEL HOLMES, General Agent.
Cable Address: Holmes, New York.
Watkins & Scott's 10th Edition Codes.
Telephone Call: 1010 Broad.

MORRIS BUILDING,
64, 66 & 68 BROAD STREET.

NEW YORK, 28th March 1893

My dear Timothy,

As you have found, where there is genius, if the work has been of a world-wide nature there is often a jealous section, ready to try and smother the most prominent worker; so that in telling such a story, the writer is beset with the necessity to disprove previous false statements, and treat with some severity those who exercise the insufferable self-complacency of treating with neglect, instead of giving prominence and respect as due.

Grandfather came from a simple, happy family life at Walbottle into the fray at Shildon, serving the Stockton and Darlington Railway. He had by then more than twenty years as a master smith, had the job of head smith at Walbottle with its more than forty smiths, carpenters and masons, with men working under him, and a reputation for work of the highest quality. George Stephenson managed to get grandfather to work for the Locomotive Manufacture he had set up to serve the needs of the Pease enterprise. He had become wrapped in the Liverpool endeavour, having exchanged his Quaker friends in Darlington for his Unitarian friends. He wriggled out from his commitments, but needed someone to deliver on them. Uncle told me that

NEW YORK AND PACIFIC STEAMSHIP, COAL AND LUMBER COMPANY
MORRIS BUILDING, 64, 66 & 68 BROAD STREET NEW YORK
Cable Address: Holmes, New York

George Stephenson's son, Robert, had taken off to South America, left his father in the lurch when the opening of the Darlington Railway was not far off. Uncle John told me Stephenson offered Timothy Hackworth a share of the company if he would come and work for him. He thought that George Stephenson was concerned that Timothy Hackworth would step out on his own.

Grandfather, after the eight years he was away from locomotives, found little changed. He was ready to come back to work on them, and George Stephenson found another way to curb any instinct grandfather had to work on his own account. He persuaded the Quakers to take on Timothy Hackworth as the Locomotive Superintendent, and eventually, manager, of the Stockton and Darlington Railway, while he Stephenson remained as Surveyor and Engineer. At the opening of the Stockton and Darlington Railway, George Stephenson led the way on the locomotive at the head while Timothy Hackworth brought up the rear, making sure that all went well with the arrangements.

When you look at the two men you must remember a successful business career must not be confused with a successful inventive, or mechanical career. An inventive, ingenious, scientific, mechanician, will, however, certainly leave his track strewn with the results of his enthusiasm. This is inevitable, and this is frequently the measuring stick to rate the man as an inventor. It requires no assertion, no defense. It is the result of the life, the work of the individual,

NEW YORK AND PACIFIC STEAMSHIP, COAL AND LUMBER COMPANY
MORRIS BUILDING, 64, 66 & 68 BROAD STREET NEW YORK
Cable Address: Holmes, New York

and it accords with the Scripture, "By their fruits shall ye know them."

The wide public, only knows what it has got. It knows how civilisation, and salvation, have followed the Railways of the world. In every line of the World's work, Transportation by Locomotive Engine has been the leading unit; has made possible the otherwise impossible. You may pass through the alphabet of the arts, sciences, manufactures, and immeasurable business life. You may join with this the joy of social life, and the climax of the spread of spiritual Christianity, and the Locomotive Engine is the Keystone, the greatest unit. This wants writing in capital letters, for a thinking world says it is true, and <u>wishes to know to whom the world owes the biggest debt of gratitude for the immeasurable benefits of the Locomotive Engine.</u>

Who can now conceive all that is meant by the first successful Locomotive? The dangers of delay that would have occurred if it had received a final check just at the turning point of its success? George Stephenson told the directors of the Darlington railway less than a year before the opening of the railway that "he does not at present see any additions can be made" to the design of the locomotive. And it would be his patron Edward Pease who would later observe, "They have placed locomotive engines on the line for haulage, before it is creditable to them, or of advantage to the Company."

NEW YORK AND PACIFIC STEAMSHIP, COAL AND LUMBER COMPANY
MORRIS BUILDING, 64, 66 & 68 BROAD STREET NEW YORK
Cable Address: Holmes, New York

And but for Royal George there would have been no turning point. The best man, the only man for that job was grandfather. Look to the Notebooks I sent Major Pangborn and any other records he has. Speak it loud and clear, <u>Timothy Hackworth was the one who made it turn.</u>

SH

NEW YORK AND PACIFIC STEAMSHIP, COAL AND LUMBER COMPANY
MORRIS BUILDING, 64, 66 & 68 BROAD STREET NEW YORK
Cable Address: Holmes, New York

Timothy laid the contents of both envelopes in front of Major Pangborn, who with the quick mind of the reporter that was never far behind all that he did, perused what Aunt Prudence and Sam Holmes had to say.

'Here's a definite prompt for you. More information about Hackworth and Stephenson, some of which probably hasn't seen the light of day before,' was Pangborn's gratified response. 'Your cousin certainly seems to grasp the spirit and scope of the Expo.'

'Major, I'm not sure how much of this is needed to show what Timothy Hackworth accomplished,' came the uncertain rejoinder. 'More importantly, I'm still short of establishing how he was acclaimed as "Father of the Locomotive". What happened at the time when my grandfather built Royal George must have been a turning point. No matter what the Stockton and Darlington Bill said, if it was a railway without an effective locomotive then it would be a dead loss.'

'Absolutely,' Major Pangborn confirmed. 'George Stephenson was about to be up against it. And he still

95

had the instincts of a battling bruiser he had shown once before in his life. He had laid his opponent low when he was challenged at the pithead. This time it was a fight about the locomotive. It was never going to be an easy ride.'

'... so they each had a place in the railways. Which is why they are both here. Here as equals. Timothy Hackworth did what was needed to take care of running the first public railway in the world – the Stockton and Darlington Railway – with locomotives built by Stephenson. George Stephenson took charge of the survey and engineering of what was to be the most high profile railway undertaking yet – the Liverpool and Manchester Railway.'

'But it all fell apart.... '

'For both men?'

'In its way I suppose you could say it did.'

CHAPTER TEN

Something had to give....

Exposition site, Same Day.

Major Pangborn wondered whether he might not have underestimated the task he had given Timothy Hackworth Young. He had accumulated for himself a wealth of information about George Stephenson, as had other visitors who sought out George Stephenson's prowess. It had taken him several visits to England and the European continent to acquire.

From the moment George Stephenson had seen the locomotive of Trevithick's design that was built in Newcastle, he was convinced he could build better and was not shy of putting that proposition forward. He had seen the unruly progress when a locomotive was put to the existing rail tracks and the damage done. He recognised the opportunity for picking the most advantageous route when laying out a new railway. The first attempts at locomotive building were a matter of trial and error, using different arrangements for the connections between the driving wheels and the pistons that were being moved by the steam generated in the boiler. Working with William Losh, he had devised a form of rail with overlapping joins that eased the path for the locomotive, reduced the bumps and was strong enough to take the weight. Working with Ralph Dodds, he had built a locomotive he called 'Blucher' that had an eight foot boiler resting on four wheels, each three feet in diameter, which were powered by two cylinders. It was capable of hauling a load of thirty tons, eight wagons at a time, full of coal, from the pit-head to the river.

It must, Pangborn reflected, have been quite a sight for people used to the horse and wagon as the way to move goods and people from one place to another. Chugging noisily along, even at a speed of only a few miles an hour, it would have been a cause for astonishment. For George Stephenson though it was a cause he saw stretching far further afield. James Watt had made a fortune from his large stationary steam engines. What promise then was there from steam engines that replaced horse power. He worked alongside Losh at his ironworks and Dodds at the coal mine, and he protected the developments to which he was a party with patents.

He was one of the first wave of pioneers and had in his grasp all that was needed of a railway builder. He understood that a combined set of three skills was required – building locomotives that provided the power, running on rails made strong enough, passing along routes cut through the countryside. He also needed patrons who were powerful enough to put their influence and their money behind his ambition.

After building a locomotive for Killingworth, he was commissioned by the Hetton Coal Company to make a railway between Hetton and the River Wear at

Sunderland. Next he would seize the opportunity to provide his services at the establishment of the Stockton and Darlington Railway, and finally his reputation would bring him the prize of the Liverpool and Manchester Railway. First a railway of eight miles, of which 3.5 miles were for locomotive, then 26 miles of single track including two stationary engines and eventually 30 miles of double track. In the space of just four short years he would be seen as the driving force of success of the first public railway in the world and then of the establishment of the first railway service between two major industrial centres. He would usher the locomotive into its part in the Industrial Revolution. He would become sought after as the 'Father of the Railways,' requested to carry out survey after survey: one between Liverpool and Birmingham, then those from London to the North and to Wales. Once brought into a view there had been a clamour for railways through England, Europe and the rest of the world such as was never seen before…

'No,' Major Pangborn mused. 'There is no shortage of information for me to draw on in bringing George Stephenson's exploits to the attention of visitors to the Transportation Department of the Columbian Exposition.'

Timothy Young however had a tougher task and was struggling. All well and good being goaded by his cousin Sam, but making sense of his grandfather's life from the documents and engineering books he had in front of him was no walk in the park. His brow was furrowed from ploughing his way through page after page of conflicting detail, which is how Major Pangborn found him.

'I'm with all these practical locomotive builders I've been reading about, Major Pangborn,' he offered. 'Much easier getting a locomotive checked over, oiled and made ready for the next trip than reading about endless scientific arguments and engineering experiments.' As he spoke he leafed his way past twenty pages of the engineering magazine he had been working through, reaching the section marked Patents. 'Look at this Major. Hundreds of patents filed in one month and seventeen of them are about locomotives. Sorting the wheat from the chaff could drive you crazy.'

'Which is exactly why there are so many early locomotive models in the B&O collection. Each step, each variation of design led forward, if not to success then to shining a light to show the way for others. Much followed on from the time when George Stephenson had a working locomotive at Killingworth mine. A demonstration of what was possible and what was promised by the iron horse.'

Major Pangborn picked up the Mechanics Magazine that had been occupying his help-mate's time, and looked down the list of patent applications that had been made. 'You are right. There were a lot of people, not just engineers, who had an inventive bent. Little though really had the same impact or lasted as long as those to do with the getting the locomotive powered up and a railway for it to run on.' He handed it back to Timothy Hackworth Young, and perched on the edge of his desk.

'Think of all that had to be gone through from the starting of the Stockton and Darlington Railway, and then that raised the stakes for the development of a railway between Liverpool and Manchester. Before you could build a railway you had to go through a lengthy procedure with the British parliament for approval. And that needed a plan laid out of the route, workings out of the cost and the money that would need to be raised, confirmation that subscribers had committed their funds, and prospects of rewards for the shareholders. Liverpool and Manchester were the two main industrial centres, importing raw materials, transporting them to the factories and the cotton mills and delivering the finished goods for export to the world. Britain was the workhorse of the world and those cities the powerhouse for trade.'

Timothy Young looked concerned. 'Wasn't what developed at Wylam of importance as well? I've been reading through Colborn's book on the principles and construction of the locomotive engine. He has the work of Hedley and Hackworth at Wylam Colliery running ahead of Stephenson.'

'Maybe, but Stephenson had his eye on a future beyond Killingworth while Hackworth already had his reputation and skill as a blacksmith to draw on. Stephenson had cut his teeth at Hetton, pulling it all together – surveying and building a railway, laying track and he had a locomotive to his patent design. When he heard that the parliamentary bill for the Stockton and Darlington Railway had passed then he sought out Edward Pease, the Quaker who had been the moving force.

It was a marriage made in heaven. Edward Pease was taken with the demeanour, the accomplishments and the vision that George Stephenson presented. And the experience he brought, reduced the risk. George had in his grasp the support he needed and, most consequentially, the money. An initial £80,000 had been contributed to set up the railway, and George Stephenson was pushing against an open door.'

The storyteller in Pangborn couldn't resist adding, 'There were tales that he had walked barefoot to Darlington, in company with Nicholas Wood, the viewer at Killingworth, to find Pease, and came to him unannounced. However it happened, he wanted to have a part in that railway and make it his own. He set aside the work already done by the surveyor, George Overton, who had laid out the route – and then set aside Overton as well. The survey was redone and changed. Taking a more direct line, the route was shortened by five miles and reduced the costs by £10,000. The Bill that had already passed through Parliament had to be revised and resubmitted. He persuaded Pease to include, for the first time in England, the possibility of using a locomotive in the running of a railway, a public railway.'

He paused. 'That... that was the beginning of the railway. That was Stephenson's masterstroke.'

Pangborn caught the look of surprise, shaded with disbelief, on Timothy Young's face. 'And not his only one. Any huckster will tell you, when you have your mark hooked, go for more. He then persuaded Edward Pease and Michael Longridge, owner of a local ironworks, that the locomotive would spread not only throughout the North of England but reach as far as London. They saw the money to be made from manufacturing locomotives and ploughed their personal money into a works to do exactly that, keeping it quite separate to the Stockton and Darlington Railway enterprise. The shares in the company were split four ways, with Robert Stephenson being included as well as his father. Shrewdly it was named after Stephenson's son who was appointed at the age of 21 to be its manager.'

'Shrewdly?' questioned Timothy Young.

'Well, George Stephenson was then free to engage in other work. Work that would lead to orders for locomotives. Orders that he could then place without apparently benefiting from the proceeds. Except, one of the conditions of setting his son up as manager was that he had to work to the designs and arrangements of his father, so he wasn't actually hands off. It just looked as though he was.'

'All this without Timothy Hackworth being involved?'

'Oh it was more far-reaching than that. Before the Stockton and Darlington line was completed and the first locomotive built, George Stephenson already had his eye on another projected railway. One that would serve the commercial interests of the huge trade between Liverpool and Manchester. Export trade of £19,000,000. Nineteen million pounds a year... A figure against which Stockton and Darlington paled into insignificance. George Stephenson had the field to himself. No other engineer or surveyor had his practical experience and, supported by Pease, he was appointed engineer and charged with completing the survey, establishing the costs and making the case for that railway.'

Timothy, who had been following all that Major Pangborn had said, commented 'And that was the start of the successful railways in England. The 15th of September in 1830 when the Liverpool and Manchester Railway opened?'

'No. The date Stephenson would never forget was five years earlier; the 17th of June 1825. One year and three weeks after he was appointed. That was when it all came crashing down round his ears.'

Timothy Young took a moment. Crashing down? That date was close to when the Stockton and Darlington Railway had opened and by then Timothy Hackworth had been appointed its Superintendent. The tumultuous reception from cheering crowds that lined the route would have been taken by both men as a measure of their success. Only added to by those that were carried in the wagons, and those who attended the celebration dinner. Adulation and approbation for all they had done. True, Timothy Hackworth had only been brought in briefly as a 'borrowed man' from Walbottle when Robert Stephenson left to go to Colombia the year before. It was George Stephenson alone who had boldly ridden at the front, champion of the line and the locomotive.

In the years that followed, Timothy Hackworth kept the four locomotives, delivered from Robert Stephenson and Co, in working order. Wagon loads of coal and goods of various sorts were carried from the coal mines to the boats on the River Tees that would take them forward. And horse power as well as locomotive power kept the line in use. The single line, with its passing points, could be subject to delays and snarl-ups, especially when the locomotives stalled or broke down or came off the line, but that, Timothy Young thought, could not be counted as 'crashing down' round anyone's ears.

'June 1825?' was the surprised response from Timothy Young. 'That date was a clear two months before the Stockton and Darlington Railway opened. What disaster could have happened then?'

Pangborn was quick to explain. 'The all important Parliamentary Bill for Liverpool and Manchester Railway was submitted, along with the survey details. That was the disaster that would shake George Stephenson and his world.' Pangborn shook his head as he contemplated the predicament George Stephenson had found himself in, 'It was known that there would be opposition. Unlike the bills for Stockton and Darlington, it was not an easy ride. George Stephenson was called to task. The owners of the canals were not going to give up their trade without a fight. Stephenson seemed to believe that his experience was sufficient to win the day. His day came, four weeks into the two-month long enquiry. Lawyers for the canal owners had a job to do.'

Timothy Young was non-plussed. 'He was working on the Liverpool and Manchester Railway survey while the Stockton and Darlington was ongoing as well?'

Major Pangborn had imagined how it must have been for the gruff man from the North. He had practical experience but that would count for little in the face of clever London lawyers. Even his rough dialect got in the way. When asked about the hazard of animals straying onto the line and getting in the way of a locomotive, he agreed in his thick Northumberland accent it would be "very ackward – for the coo." He thought he had dealt with any possible objection, but the response was ridiculed and he and the "coo" were made the butt of jokes among the lawyers. Worse was to come. So far as the practicalities of the route were concerned, he had relied on assistants to carry out the measurements and they got it wrong. Giving evidence he was found out. Deficiencies and absurdities were mercilessly exposed. The summing up from the lawyer was brutal – "I say he never had a plan – I believe he never had one – I do not believe he is capable of making one… He is either ignorant or something else which I will not mention." Neither Stephenson nor the Bill survived that encounter. No-one was going to easily rely on his word alone after such a public humiliation.

Major Pangborn thought that Timothy Hackworth Young was partially right. 'Maybe he took on too much. The Bill failed. He failed. The profits of the canal owners were not going to be prised away from them. The Board of the Liverpool and Manchester Railway had to take a different approach to get their project approved. Engineers with sound reputations were brought in to re-survey the route. Landowners and canal owners were placated – compensated in different ways. George Stephenson was given his marching orders.'

'That must have been a blow,' said Timothy Young. 'Not many would have pressed on after that. Is that when my grandfather came to the rescue?'

'Well George Stephenson still had those who championed his cause. And the Stockton and Darlington Railway was soon to come into its own. The first working railway open for public use. Your grandfather had the superintendent's job of keeping it running, while Stephenson was designated engineer. And Stephenson was bathed in the glory of that enterprise when it opened.'

Major Pangborn had, like many others, made a point of following the progress of the Liverpool and Manchester Railway after the discovery that the appointment of George Stephenson and the path to the development of the famous locomotive Rocket was not without its problems. In just less than a year later, a second Liverpool and Manchester Bill was considered and approved. The long-established engineers, the Rennie brothers, and the surveyor, Vignobles, succeeded where Stephenson had failed. It would have been expected they would then be the ones to oversee and drive the plan through, but they had conditions for doing that. They insisted on appointing the engineer for the work. However, they emphatically declined working with George Stephenson.

'The Stockton and Darlington Railway wasn't long open before George Stephenson was recalled to the Liverpool and Manchester Railway. The Board were decided on the need, above all other considerations, for his practical experience. And the influential Unitarians were on his side. So too the commercial instincts of the Darlington Quakers.'

Timothy Young heard the tone of admiration in Major Pangborn's voice. George Stephenson seemed to have had his own personal resurrection, although he would have been unlikely to see it in those terms.

'Oh, George Stephenson came back from that setback but not until the return of his son from his South American adventure,' Pangborn added. 'There was still a long way to go before locomotives would run between Liverpool and Manchester.'

'One back on the clever lawyers then. He would have pressed on to prove them all wrong,' Timothy concluded, wondering what else could have lain in wait for his grandfather and George Stephenson.

Major Pangborn handed back to Timothy Young the copy of the Mechanics Journal that had started this conversation, with a reassuring 'I'm sure you can put flesh on your aunt's comments about Hackworth and the Stockton and Darlington Railway.'

Timothy Young had gleaned what he needed from some of the reports and publications Major Pangborn had left with him. Early on at Wylam, Blacket, the owner, and Hedley, the viewer, and Timothy Hackworth were involved in the developments of the locomotive. A key experiment was made to establish that the weight of the locomotive was sufficient alone to provide adequate friction, removing once and for all time the need for chains and cogs and any other device to deliver the driving force. Wylam was the place where first Puffing Billy was built and then the Wylam Dilly. The locomotives there replaced the horse and oxen previously used to draw the wagons full of coal to the river. George Stephenson too had worked on building various types of locomotive, finally settling on Blucher. They followed along the same lines, except that at Wylam they had fashioned a boiler that returned on itself, giving a greater heating surface than the boiler of any locomotive constructed at Killingworth.

From what Aunt Prudence and Sam Holmes had said, Stephenson went on to build a reputation as a builder of railways. Resting on his laurels and holding to his patented locomotive design. Timothy Hackworth had a reputation as a builder too, respected in the area for his skills in fabrication and his position as foreman smith at Walbottle. They were both drawn to the Stockton and Darlington endeavour.

That history settled, Timothy Young sought out a description of the birth of Royal George that had followed. He turned to the pages of Colborn's treatise until he found the account of Timothy Hackworth's time at the Stockton and Darlington Railway.

"Hackworth determined to alter and improve one of the engines then in for repairs..." he read. "This engine, when altered, was known as the 'Royal George', and commenced working in October, 1827." There followed a detailed description of the locomotive that Hackworth devised, two years after the opening of the railway.

"The return flue of the Wylam engines was adopted, and a liberal amount of heating surface thus obtained. There were six coupled wheels, 4 feet in diameter, and the cylinders, which were placed vertically at the end opposite to the fire place were 11 inches in diameter; the stroke of the pistons being 20 inches, the piston rods worked downward, and were connected to the front pair of wheels." And a special reference was made to those measurements. "Hackworth's engine... was a bold departure from the practice of the period; and its maker thus led the way in respect of one of the most important proportions of the modern locomotive."

Colborn went on to describe other various novel features that were first introduced in the engine, and the details of the 'blast-pipe' sent by Hackworth's son "some time ago to *The Engineer* newspaper, and were published in that journal August 14, 1857."

It was not by chance that Timothy Hackworth designed and built Royal George. He had been the one who repaired and rebuilt the locomotives supplied from the Stephenson works; had seen the deficiencies in their construction and performance and seen for himself the extent to which the operation of the railway suffered. But he was the superintendent not the engineer, and George Stephenson had already intimated there was no further developments needed for his locomotives. Edward Pease and others of the railway committee saw their finances stretched.

Colborn recorded that the railway "in addition to stationary engines and horse power, had five locomotive engines, four of which were from Stephenson's factory. They gave unsatisfactory results, and in 1827 the directors were understood to have seriously considered the propriety of abandoning locomotives altogether, when Hackworth determined to alter and improve one of the engines then in for repair."

Royal George was the result; a phoenix raised from the ashes. It proved itself capable of hauling twenty-four loaded wagons, weighing 100 tons, and above all, as it was engineered to the standards of a master smith, proved more reliable.

There was nothing here that could be described as 'crashing around the ears' of Timothy Hackworth, though it hardly shone a good light on the mechanical engineering prowess of the Stephenson locomotive works. Timothy Hackworth had spoken out when the need for his skill was self-evident; he had saved the locomotive from being set aside; he had changed the fortunes of the railway that he served.

Timothy Young needed to find out more about the impact of the locomotive and picked up one of the reference books that Major Pangborn had left with him. 'The IMPERIAL CYCLOPAEDIA of MACHINERY' that had been published in the wake of the 1851 Great Exhibition. The frontpiece was graced with a bust of the renowned James Watt, that was followed on the next page by a dedication to respected engineer, Robert Napier, and the encyclopaedia was described as including descriptive letterpress, an essay on the Steam Engine, and a History of the Railways of Great Britain and America. A suitably serious account of all things mechanical.

The first article was headed 'The STEAM-ENGINE: Stationary, Locomotive and Marine' and was introduced with a quotation from a Dr Dionysius Lardner – who had much to say about locomotives. "The history of the STEAM-ENGINE offers to our notice a series of contrivances which, for exquisite and refined ingenuity, stand without any parallel in the annals of MECHANICAL SCIENCE. To enumerate the benefits it has conferred, would be to count almost every comfort and every luxury of life. It has increased the sum of human happiness, not only by calling new pleasures into existence, but by so cheapening former enjoyments as to render them attainable by those who before could never have hoped to share them ..."

It was not until more than 50 pages into the lengthy article that the story of Timothy Hackworth and Royal George was told.

"She was named the "Royal George", and commenced working in October,1827. As an exposition of her superiority over the horses – which, be it remembered were at this time in the ascendent as regards their employment on railways – we may compare the actual results of the two systems of working.

Cost of "Royal George," £425; number of tons conveyed by her in one year (1828), 22,442 tons over twenty miles; cost of conveyance, 1/4d. per ton per mile, or, including all repairs and maintenance, and interest on sunk capital, at 10 per cent, £466; an economy in working which is rarely exceeded at the present day, after a lapse of twenty-three years. The cost of the same work performed by horses was £998, showing a difference of £532 in favour of this engine over the animal power."

So, Timothy Young thought, with the Royal George locomotive, Hackworth turned the economics round for the Stockton and Darlington Railway. Smiling to himself, he imagined how this information would strike the visitors to the Exposition. In his mind's eye he already saw the display he was going to make of this to set alongside the portrait of his grandfather. He read on.

"The points of improvement in the "Royal George" which conduced to this important result, evidencing not only her great superiority over her compeers, but the vast resources of the imperfectly developed locomotive system, were simply these :—-the increased evaporative surface of the boiler; the perfect command over heavy loads in all states of the weather, by reason of the superior tractive adhesion derived from the six coupled wheels; and the introduction of the blast pipe, an invention which alone will carry down the name of Hackworth to future ages in connection with early locomotive history."

Sam Holmes had been right. Royal George was the stamp their grandfather had put on a crucial stage of development of the locomotive. His skill and inventiveness had resulted in a locomotive that above all others set the railway back on track. And a final observation set the seal on that.

"Up to the period of which we write, no really efficient locomotive was in use, as the steam pressure invariably fell, in spite of the best efforts of the driver; and the superiority of the "Royal George," in this respect alone, at once elevated it far above its contemporaries, for it was capable of maintaining a speed of nine miles per hour throughout its run of twenty miles, in all weathers."

The results spoke for themselves so far as Hackworth was concerned, and so far as the locomotive drivers were concerned, and for the Stockton and Darlington Railway. That was the step forward the locomotive would have been waiting for. That would be the start of the story Timothy Young would tell. Royal George with its power and reliability would be seen as the benchmark, one that had set the locomotives of Stephenson & Co in the shade.

He couldn't help remaining concerned though as to what was going to come crashing round the ears of Timothy Hackworth.

CHAPTER ELEVEN

Building Railways

Exposition site, Monday 3rd April 1893

Major Pangborn opened the box that Brigham had brought for him and looked carefully over the folders which housed the maps and plans of the Liverpool and Manchester Railway he had collected in his travels. The first ill-fated submission to parliament had, after several years of plans and planning, finally been made in 1825. A year later it had been revised, resubmitted and finally been approved in May 1826. Money had helped to buy off the opposition, an accurate survey had been completed and a costing of the work involved had been subject to a more realistic estimate.

Work had started in June the same year but it would be September 1830 before it was completed and the railway opened. Even though he had been brought back to engineer the project, the criticisms must have been still ringing in George Stephenson's ears – "I say he never had a plan – I believe he never had one – I do not believe he is capable of making one..." If the lawyers had been right and George Stephenson did not have a plan then the construction of the 30-mile railway would prove a trial – a severe test of his determination.

The report of the construction from Henry Booth, secretary to the railway and co-designer with George Stephenson of Rocket, made it sound like a walk in the park.

> "A few hundred yards to the south of the town, the Railway crosses a narrow valley by a short but lofty embankment, and a handsome bridge of four arches, each 40 feet span. Under the eastern arch the turn pike road passes from Newton to Warrington, and beneath another arch flows a stream which turns an old corn mill, immediately below the bridge. Adjacent also, is situate one of those antique mansions, built in the ancient baronial style, whose white exterior, with black oak crossings, and pointed gables, harmonizes well with the rude scenery around."

The pages of this description of the line made it as much to be wondered at as did his own travelogue for the Baltimore and Ohio railway. In his own account he had used graphic images to tell a story, which he found often counted for more than any number of his words, no matter how well crafted. Depicting the viaduct at Relay, the Point of Rocks showing the train running alongside the Potomac river, and the Buckhorn Wall that towered above the track near the picturesque village of Rowlesburg beyond the summer resort of Deer Park, had all made the adventure of railway travel seem more real. There were just as dramatic vistas of the Liverpool and Manchester Railway he could use as memorial to the works of George Stephenson.

He looked to the etched images he had of the features of the Liverpool to Manchester line: The tunnel at the station entrance, the Sankey viaduct, the Skew Bridge, Chat Moss and Olive Mount Cutting. Features that were each a formidable challenge; a huge step by George Stephenson into the unknown; the uncharted realms of an engineering undertaking for the largest railway yet built.

Major Pangborn read again what Henry Booth, Secretary to the Liverpool and Manchester Railway, had written for posterity:

> "the passenger by this new line of route having to traverse the deepest recesses, where the natural surface of the ground is the highest, and being mounted on the loftiest ridges and highest embankments, riding above the tops of the trees, and overlooking the surrounding country, where the natural surface of the ground is the lowest, -this peculiarity and this variety being occasioned by that essential requisite in a well constructed Railway—a level line — imposing the necessity of cutting through the high lands and embanking across the low; thus, in effect, presenting to the traveler all the variety of mountain and ravine in pleasing succession..."

It was all very well for Booth to provide an inviting description of travelling on the railway – which he could well use in the display of George Stephenson's works – but it did not say enough about the enormity of the work that was undertaken.

The railway had to be forced through the countryside, sometimes under the land, sometimes over waterways and turn pike roads. A force of thousands, thousands of navvies, would take to the way with little more than shovels, picks and barrows to change the face of the land through human strength. Tunnels, bridges, embankments were all the same to them. Bruising and brutish hard labour. And someone had to make sure it kept to plan, that a way was always found to move forward beyond the hazards. That was a challenge which George Stephenson's son, Robert, left behind when he took his three year adventure to the silver mines of the Americas. It was one that George Stephenson took on alone.

Started right after the Bill was passed, the tunnel that led down to the ending of the railway under Liverpool was more than a mile long, and was constructed in eight separate lengths. The first shaft was opened in September 1826 and a way twenty-two feet wide for the track and sixteen feet high had to be tunnelled. The etching Pangborn had obtained showed teams of navvies working by candlelight in dreadful conditions. In parts they had encountered the hazard of soft blue shale and wet sand, water draining through and streaming underfoot, props holding back the roof above until brick arches could be formed. He also knew that the work was carried out day and night throughout 1827; carving out a route and removing the spoil, pressing forward, keeping to a plan for the alignment of the sections. It was the end of the year before even two-thirds of the tunnel was completed, and it would be June the following year when the directors were advised the aligned sections were joined up.

The contrast with the work at Olive Mount was abundant. Here it was all in the open. A ravine to hold a two-mile long stretch of railway was hewn through the rocks. Someone had captured how it had been at that time, and Pangborn had a graphic depiction of the scale of it. Men were shown as they clambered up and down the rock face, relying on rickety wooden ladders that in stages reached down nearly seventy feet from the ground above. A precarious clambering about which they would have had to face in all weathers as pieces of rock were dislodged and the track was formed.

And where the roadway and the railway crossed swords, had to cross over each other, there were stone bridges to be built. No-one was going to change the route of the road. Nor was the route of the railway up for variation. In one place the two had to cross at an angle to keep to their respective alignments. Stephenson chose to build a bridge on the skew to solve the problem, which in its turn meant that the bridge had to be bigger, wider by more than twenty feet than the railway required, and each stone had to be cut to an angle to fit into its place. The picture Pangborn had of the Skew Bridge made that clear.

The challenge of crossing over the Sankey canal was monumental. A giant viaduct carried the locomotives high above the canal; nine arches, each with a fifty-foot span, stretched for more than two hundred yards over the canal at a height of seventy feet. High enough that the ships and vessels below could unfurl their sails and make best speed. Pangborn could only imagine the sight that would have greeted passengers in the locomotives as they looked to the horizon and watched the slow progress of the canal traffic. He looked at the etched picture he had of the viaduct, and then at the final one of those that he had acquired. One of the notorious Chat Moss. The contrast between the grandeur of the Sankey Bridge and the barren expanse of the bog that was Chat Moss could not have been sharper.

George Stephenson had been pilloried for his rash statement that he would traverse Chat Moss but without specifying exactly how. He had needed a solution different to that envisaged by the engineer who gave evidence in the ill-fated Parliamentary Bill. His testimony Booth had highlighted in his report about construction of the line:

"it was contended that the Canals and River were capacious enough for all the traffic of the port; that, moreover, our levels and sections were erroneous; that the Locomotive Engine was an unsightly object; and that the formation of the Railway would cost three or four times as much as the estimate: nay, Mr. Francis Giles, Civil Engineer, was produced to record his opinion that it would cost upwards of £200,000 to carry the Railway across Chat Moss alone:—from all which it followed, that, from considerations of kindness to the Proprietors of so wild and impracticable a scheme, the Bill ought to be rejected by the legislature."
* I subjoin an abstract from Mr. Giles' evidence before the Committee of the House of Commons, on the 5th May, 1825, taken from an official copy:—

Q. Be so good as to tell us whether in your judgment a Rail-road of this description can be safely made over Chat Moss, without going to the bottom of the Moss.

A. I say certainly not.

Q. Will it be necessary, therefore, in making a Rail-road which is to stand, to take out, along the whole line of the road, the whole of the Moss to the bottom?

A. Undoubtedly.

Q. Will that make it necessary to cut down the 33 or 34 feet of which you have been speaking?

A. Yes.

Q. And afterwards to fill it up with other soil?

A. To such a height as the Rail-road is to be carried; other soil mixed with a portion of the Moss.

..

Q. But suppose they were to work upon this stuff, could they get their carriages to the place.

A. No carriage can stand on the Moss short of the bottom.

Q. What would they do to make it stand—laying planks, or something of that sort?

A. Nothing would support it.

Q. So that, if you could carry a Rail-road on this fluid stuff – if you could do it – it would still take a great number of men, and a great sum of money. Could it be done, in your opinion, for £6000?

A. I should say £200,000 would not get through it.

Q. My Learned Friend wishes to know what it would cost to lay it with diamonds?

And it was work on crossing Chat Moss that had been started first. Before any line could be constructed an attempt had to be made to stabilise the ground. Many thousands of cubic yards of spoil was tipped into it, all of which gradually and silently disappeared into the bog. In the October of 1826 members of the Board went and inspected progress for themselves. In April 1827, engineer Wilson was called in and inspected the work and was able to report favourably to them. The crossing of the bog only finally happened in January 1830. In truth it had actually taken men years of working before the first trial of the locomotive travelling across Chat Moss could take place.

For the most part across the barren waste of four miles, the railway virtually floated; floated on rafts of brushwood and heather, laid under the wood sleepers which supported the rails. Writing in 1837, Stephenson had typically made it seem a victory of one man's confidence over general doubt: 'Even my assistants began to feel uneasy and to doubt the success of the scheme. The directors, too, spoke of it as a hopeless task... There was no help, however, but to go on. An immense outlay had been incurred and a great loss would have been occasioned had the scheme then been abandoned, and the line taken by another route.'

George Stephenson was 'hands on' at every point of the 30 miles of the line. He appointed three assistants, each to cover a part of the railway line, but set himself a punishing schedule. Riding on horse back the length of the works during the day, making notes, then in the evening recording detail plans of work to be done, ending with dictating copious letters. Everything was in his charge, and he alone was the person who had authorised and commissioned works as they were needed. George Stephenson was a law to himself.

His encouragement to his men, as with much else, was to 'Persevere' and, despite the setbacks, he remained firm in his belief that the locomotive would prevail. When all the accounting was done, the total costs and expenses for Chat Moss were recorded as less than twenty thousand pounds – a triumph for George Stephenson in every way. The payoff for his very singular way of working and managing the challenges.

Major Pangborn thought he could do justice to George Stephenson the railway builder, telling the story of the formidable challenge of driving a railway between the two principal centres that traded merchandise with the world. He recognized in Stephenson a man with an affinity to Christopher Columbus; both had a vision of a brave new world and sufficient presence to persuade others to commit to their adventures.

Unlike Columbus's historic crossing of the ocean, those who funded the Liverpool and Manchester Railway could see how Stephenson was progressing as time went by; how well he was closing in on the work being done. At the start of 1829 there had been another report commissioned, this time by Thomas Telford, an accomplished engineer, which catalogued the shortcomings of Stephenson's style. Only 19 of the 58 bridges required had been built and he estimated that a further £200,000 was needed for all the outstanding works. That in addition to an extra £100,000 loan already taken up over and above the £400,000 subscribed by original shareholders. Lack of control and nonexistent financial management was the price the directors of the Liverpool and Manchester Railway paid for the vision and unrelenting determination of their engineering superintendent. Their focus would turn to matters they could more comfortably address, that of turning the railway into a commercial enterprise.

George Stephenson also had his eyes set firmly on the future, branching out beyond the achievements of this great undertaking. He looked for any means to ensure the future of the locomotive building company that was in the name of his son, Robert, but was still a George Stephenson enterprise. George Stephenson and Co, surveyors and builders of railways was also set up; getting a foothold in the birth of other railway beginnings prompted by the success of Stockton and Darlington Railway.

* * *

The fanfare of the opening of the Stockton and Darlington Railway had sounded around the world and set the stage. Visitors came from far and wide eager to see for themselves at first hand what had been accomplished by three men: Edward Pease who had driven the proposal through Parliament and raised the finance, George Stephenson the engineer who had set the line and built the locomotives and Timothy Hackworth who pulled it all together and made it work. The use of the power of the horse for transport had been supplanted by the marvel of the steam locomotive. And there were others from America and from Europe who wanted to emulate what had been accomplished in Britain. Among the visitors had been Marc Seguin from France.

Marc Seguin was well on the way to introducing a railway into France which, like other countries, was intent on gaining British expertise for their own benefit. On the one hand he met George Stephenson who succeeded so often in painting an over -optimistic picture of what he and his locomotives were capable of achieving. On the other side was Edward Pease who saw the day-to-day workings of the locomotive building enterprise faltering – a situation that he had communicated to Robert Stephenson in no uncertain terms:

'I can assure thee that thy business at Newcastle, as well as thy father's engineering, have suffered very much from thy absence, and, unless, thou soon return, the former will be given up, as Mr Longridge is not able to give it that attention it requires: and what is done is not done with credit to the house.'

George Stephenson had a plan, and a necessity to take advantage of the potential orders for locomotives for Robert Stephenson & Co from the French man. Marc Seguin too had a plan.

France was ready to encourage the importation of technology that offered economic benefit. Two sample products, devices or machines would be allowed to be purchased and not incur the 50 per cent import duties, provided that the purpose was to obtain a springboard to emulation and the development of skills by French companies. Seguin sought to purchase one locomotive for his works in Lyon, and the other for the workshops of mechanic Alexis Hallette in Arras. Both locomotives were to be delivered to the French sites, and the workforces there would undertake the re-construction of the locomotives themselves from the parts and sections that had been sent across the Channel. To help seal the deal and get the locomotives he wanted from the manufacturer he wanted, Seguin dangled the carrot of this being the first part of an order for 30 such locomotives. He visited more than once, placed that initial order with Robert Stephenson and Co in the spring of 1827 but it was not until Robert returned from his South American adventure that they would be built. They were constructed at the end of spring the following year, delivered in parts to Seguin's Perrache works at the end of July and worked on there during August and September.

What Seguin found was that when put to the line the Stephenson locomotives could not haul the loads as he had been shown. The two men had caught each other out with promises that neither could fulfill. And Seguin resorted to the development of his multi-tubular boiler that he had patented in February 1828, but that was not constructed and tried until January 1829. He later redesigned his locomotive, completing it in September 1829. Seguin found that his locomotive No 1 weighed considerably less than the Stephenson locomotive, it performed better and the price of construction by his workforce in Lyon was around 50 per cent of that from Hallette or from Robert Stephenson & Co. Final trials, because of the weather, were not undertaken until October 3, by which time the Stephensons had built, run and established the credentials of Rocket using the same design concept.

Major Pangborn in all this saw in George Stephenson a man driven by ambition. A man who over-egged the cake, who promised more than he could deliver. He had perhaps in his enthusiasm pulled the wool over people's eyes, but he would have realised that for the weight and extent of goods to be hauled he would need more and better than had been developed so far. His estimate was that 30 locomotives would be required for the Liverpool and Manchester Railway. He had of necessity sought new approaches. New locomotives – and new means.

George Stephenson had had to rein back his claims before giving evidence for the first Liverpool and Manchester Railway Bill that a speed of 20mph would be achieved – it might have seemed reasonable to his mind but it had stretched the credibility of others. Not only was there concern that the locomotive might frighten the horses but it had been suggested that travelling at such a speed passengers would be deprived of the very air they needed to survive. His position was not made any easier by the assertions of Nicholas Wood, long-time friend and supporter of Stephenson, in his respected treatise on the locomotive. He held that the cause of the locomotive was not helped by such extravagant and impossible claims about the speed that could be achieved. None of which had helped in deciding how best to power the transport of goods on the Manchester and Liverpool Railway.

The new approaches taken by George Stephenson had led to the creation of two quite distinct locomotives; the Twin Sisters and the Lancashire Witch.

The Twin Sisters was specifically intended for use during the construction of the railway. It was as different to the prevailing design as had been Timothy Hackworth's Royal George. On a six-wheel frame were placed two dumpy-looking vertical boilers; supposedly to enable the locomotive to work on severe inclines, avoiding the difficulty of running out of steam, or danger of explosion, because of insufficient water above the heat source. Standing tall each boiler had it's own chimney, hence the name; each the same height as those on previous locomotives, but two-thirds the girth.

The Lancashire Witch, a locomotive mounted on four wheels and with two flues, was a new design by his son and was Stephenson's hope for his ambitions. It was also the locomotive about which he wrote to Timothy Hackworth – the Blast Pipe letter. The one that described Stephenson's satisfaction with the use and reliance on bellows as the means of providing additional draught and excitement to the passage of air through the firebox.

Both locomotives would do useful work to assist in removing spoil and ballast from the working sites of the railway as it was constructed, and Lancashire Witch would be transferred to work the Bolton and Leigh line. That would be the time when what it could accomplish could be demonstrated.

Major Pangborn had seen the comments about such demonstrations made by engineer Mr Philips, and recorded in Hansard in March 1825:

'As to the second assertion, that the average time consumed in proceeding from Manchester to Liverpool by water was 36 hours, he understood the fact to be, that by the Mersey and Irwell canal, the time occupied was twelve hours, and that by new arrangements the time would be reduced to nine or ten. With respect to celerity of carriage, they had been told, that on these rail-roads goods were conveyed at the rate of 10 or 12 miles an hour, while on canals the average was four miles an hour. This assertion had been repeated over and over again in pamphlets and newspapers; and, in proof of its truth, an experiment was publicly made. The advocates of the rail-road appointed a day for trying the experiment, with a loco-motive carriage, and the trustees of the rail-road, as well as others who were interested in the business, attended. Now, what was the result? After a fortnight's preparation, and having selected the best loco-motive engine they could find, the average rate, on a plane surface, was not three miles and three quarters per hour, and on an inclination it was not more than four miles and a half per hour. This experiment had completely failed. But when those persons only were present who had no reason to take a very accurate account of the business, a second experiment was made, and then the rate was said to have been doubled.'

Perhaps, Major Pangborn thought, it was to avoid charges such as those of Mr Philips, or any other engineer of the day, that led Robert Stephenson to put on a final show in public when the trial was made to establish whether it would be locomotives or stationary steam engines that would be used haul the goods from Liverpool to Manchester and back.

Working with both Stephensons and bringing fresh ideas to that same end was a man immersed in the railway and all that it promised – Henry Booth, one of the early promoters of the railway, Secretary to the board of the Liverpool and Manchester Railway, another champion of George Stephenson, and like him, a Unitarian.

In 1829, the time was fast approaching when a decision had to be made by the directors of the Liverpool and Manchester Railway about what would be used as the means of hauling wagons full of goods along their railway. Booth and other directors were with the locomotive, though the opinion of George Stephenson alone was not going to be relied on. A visit to see for themselves how the locomotive was being used in practice had been made, but there was no single view as to what would best serve the interests of the company – the locomotive or stationary steam engines. That was the point at which the matter was put into the hands of two respected expert engineers, charged with visiting, collecting information, establishing costs and coming to a definite recommendation. On the 12th of January, 1829, the Board of Directors in Liverpool authorised a visit of inspection by James Walker and John Urpeth Rastrick to the various operational railways in the North East.

The failure of the first Parliamentary Bill had shown George Stephenson that what was done and said was open to scrutiny in a stricter fashion than was ever encountered at Killingworth, or Hetton or Stockton and Darlington. He made sure he accompanied the two engineers to the Bolton & Leigh line to show what his latest locomotive was capable of undertaking. There was one report given of a trial that, for Walker, had to be discounted. It would have required him to believe that Lancashire Witch was a 24 Horsepower locomotive. A later review of its performance in normal use, established it performed at 11 Horse power. A calculation that for him more closely corresponded with its 66 square feet of heating surface, and seven-ton weight. The prospective use of that locomotive, and the extent to which it would meet the requirements of the directors of the Liverpool and Manchester Railway, was going to be compared to others already in operational use, and to other ways of working.

On the 9th of the following March, their reports on the comparative merits of the two systems as they found them were laid before the directors. The outcome, the Walker and Rastrick reports to the board, had been seen by Major Pangborn. He could imagine the looks of consternation on the faces of the directors when they first read it, and the heated discussions that ensued. In the glare of such a public concern as the Liverpool and Manchester Railway there was little room for manoeuvre.

CHAPTER TWELVE

Trials and tribulations

Exposition site, Same day

Rastrick and Walker had discharged their instructions to the letter. What, they had been asked, in all circumstances, is the best description of moving power to be employed upon Liverpool and Manchester Railway. They visited, they made notes about performance, they raised questions about repairs, they discussed and they came to a definite conclusion. Walker described the burden of their responsibilities:

> "The comparative advantages of the different kinds of power applicable to Rail-roads generally, is at the present time a very interesting question, the difficulty and importance of which, as a matter of science, are much increased by the magnitude of your concern, and by the various considerations necessary to be embraced and balanced previously to arriving at any decision that would be useful to you, or consistent with the confidence you have placed in us."

They had to determine whether the wagon-loads of goods should be powered by large steam engines, set at one-and-a half-mile intervals, standing in tall engine buildings. Should the wagons have long ropes attached to them and be hauled along the lines by such a series of powerful stationary steam engines winding in the ropes? Or should they be hauled by separate steam locomotives, each locomotive attached directly to the wagons and run under its own steam along the lines. The import of Walker's words became even more evident as they were applied to the primary object of their inquiry, the comparative expense of conveying goods upon a railway by locomotive and fixed engines. The two engineers were quite clear in their conclusion:

> "annual expenses is nearly as 7 to 9 in favour of the stationary system."

Major Pangborn recognised that outcome for what it was, another huge setback for George Stephenson, and for his supporters. Here he was conquering the geography, putting his stamp across the land but unable to persuade the directors of the enterprise he worked for that he was right. That the locomotive would do all that was asked of it, and make their merchants and traders all more wealthy... and now two respected engineers, one of whom was engaged in building locomotives, had damned their use of the locomotive. And, despite the progress he had made with the Lancashire Witch, this brush with science must have left him demoralised, disadvantaged; it certainly left him and his plans at a crossroads. There was no merit for George Stephenson in having a railway without locomotives to run on it.

The two engineers had been sceptical of the results of 'experiments' arranged by interested parties, even of

Robert Stephenson's runs with Timothy Hackworth's Royal George and especially the reported performance of Lancashire Witch. It was the son, Robert Stephenson, who joined the fray, deploying all his argumentative skill and scientific knowledge to prove the engineers wrong. He would look to Timothy Hackworth for support, the performance of whose six-wheeled locomotive the two engineers had made particular reference as to its prowess and power. Time for Major Pangborn to make sure Hackworth's grandson could tell that part of the story.

NEW YORK AND PACIFIC STEAMSHIP, COAL
AND LUMBER COMPANY.

DIRECT STEAMSHIP LINE
BETWEEN
NEW YORK AND PACIFIC COAST.
MONTHLY SAILINGS.

SAMUEL HOLMES, General Agent.
Cable Address: Holmes, New York.
Watkins & Scott's 10th Edition Codes.
Telephone Call: 1010 Broad.

MORRIS BUILDING,
64, 66 & 68 BROAD STREET.

NEW YORK, 5th April 1893

Dear Timothy,

What good news you have. Major Pangborn was right to suggest that 'Royal George' should be centre stage of the story to be told about grandfather. It was the making of the Stockton and Darlington Railway, as was his skill and know-how. He knew every man, every locomotive, every bump and jump of the rails, every siding, every stationary engine.

They all relied on grandfather; George Stephenson did, Robert Stephenson certainly did and even Edward Pease. And he wrote to grandfather asking him to make sure the works and the men were neat and tidy looking when visitors came, and asked him to have all his calculations at the ready. There had been visitors from far and wide ever since the opening, and grandfather was always open about what he knew, what he could pass on to others – he had no belief in patents.

You will find what you need in the copies of the correspondence I sent over. Robert Stephenson went to war over the findings of Walker and Rastrick, reached out to grandfather as the one man in the country whose experience would be listened to. There is one letter, dated March 17, 1829, when he sounds in desperate need of grandfather's assistance, and there is grandfather's reply three weeks later. The directors of the Liverpool and Manchester Railway came to their final decision less than two weeks after.

Keep up the good work. The world will soon have grandfather's name on their lips whenever they talk about the locomotive.

SH

NEW YORK AND PACIFIC STEAMSHIP, COAL AND LUMBER COMPANY
MORRIS BUILDING, 64, 66 & 68 BROAD STREET NEW YORK
Cable Address: Holmes, New York

Exposition site, Thursday 6th April 1893

Timothy Young had indeed listened to what Major Pangborn had to say about the progress with the Liverpool and Manchester Railway and how, while the cause of the locomotive had been sorely tested, Hackworth's Royal George had been favourably received. Sam's letter was all the encouragement he needed. Timothy laid his other paperwork to one side and first set himself to read the documents the Major had left with him.

He started with the report from Walker and Rastrick to the directors of the Liverpool and Manchester Railway. The Major had been right. The engineers had described Royal George as "undoubtedly the most powerful that has yet been made." They still had reason to be cautious about results put forward to them. They only trusted what they saw for themselves. It was not unknown for optimistic results to be contrived one way or another. They would discount such results on the grounds that to achieve them the locomotive had been stretched to its very limit and would not sustain that performance over the length of the 30 miles of this, the longest railway yet. Walker and Rastrick used the science that was evolving to calculate each locomotive's power, expressed as the equivalent in horse power, and from that drew up the load that could realistically be hauled at 10 miles per hour. They calculated that the number of locomotives needed was more than three times that which George Stephenson had claimed was sufficient.

Their reasoning left Timothy Young cold. No one nowadays would quite understand where they were coming from or the 'science' they claimed to employ. He turned from their extensive written arguments and ploughed instead through the report that was made under the names of Robert Stephenson and Joseph Locke. It became clear from the tone that, if the locomotive was to survive, fire was being fought with fire.

Timothy Young had to smile at the convoluted arguments. Robert Stephenson could certainly marshall the facts and the arguments, questioning the conventional wisdoms of the times while at the same time keeping to the same basics as Walker and Rastrick. He had taken great pains to set forward a scientific argument about determining the power of a locomotive, showed there were better ways of calculating a value, more appropriate criteria to employ. Robert accepted their definition of a horse power; 150 lbs moving at a rate of two-and-a-half-miles per hour. He also conceded, in comparing the two forms of engine, that locomotives used more fuel than stationary engines to produce the same effect. But that was where he stopped. Friction, fuel and number of locomotives on the one hand, were set against the hazards of an extended series of stationary engines, the ropes needed, their weight, size, durability and friction. All his figures were based on those from actual operational use, not overall averages or calculated, as Timothy Young noted. He drew up for himself a list of the points on which Robert Stephenson took practical issue with Walker and Rastrick:

The case for the locomotive:

Friction force holding back the power - Walker arrived at a figure of twelve and a half pounds per ton of goods hauled; Robert used the figure of eleven and one fifth pounds established by Nicholas Woods at Killingworth;

Hauling power of 10 Horse Power locomotive - Walker calculated it as 13 tons, Robert's revised figure was 15 1/3 tons based on performance of his latest locomotive design at Bolton;

Fuel consumption - Walker had used an average that included 'old' locomotives,

Robert's calculation gave a difference of half a pound less per ton per mile.

All factors reducing the costs for the use of locomotives.

<u>The case against the stationary engine:</u>
Friction of ropes - Walker carried out experiments, which Robert Stephenson chided him for not specifying the circumstances and conditions just as Walker had chided him and discounted his results, arriving at 1/22 of the weight of the rope. Robert cited 1/10 as the correct proportion based on his own experiments;

Walker determined that a rope of three and a half inches circumference was strong enough, costing upwards of £11,000 per annum, or about one-third of the whole expense. Robert gave evidence that a more costly rope of four and a half inches would be required.

There were arguments about stopping and starting for passengers and goods en route, about effect of rain on the weight of rope, about the complexities of a system for managing men and carriages without mishaps, delays.

All factors increasing the costs of using stationary engines throughout the thirty miles of railway.

Timothy Young as he went through the pages of arguments and schedules of figures also particularly noted that Walker and Rastrick had added the considerable sum of

£3000 specifically for construction works for stationary engines at Chat Moss. He could not see how the two engineers imagined that huge stationary engines could be sited anywhere across the bog, yet alone operate with mile-and-a-half lengths of rope and the men to work them. The point that Robert made about practical experience being superior to any scientific or theoretic appraisal was well made.

At every turn of their pronouncements Robert Stephenson had challenged and refuted the basis of the work of Walker and Rastrick. He had reduced the capital costs of the locomotive to £73,000, while the equivalent for stationary engines had risen to £121,500. There had been a similar impact on running costs for the two modes of power. His conclusion ran completely counter to theirs:

> "the comparison of annual expenses is nearly as 8 to 5 in favour of the locomotive."

Cousin Sam would have had a field day with such a battering of the engineer's pronouncements, yet Robert Stephenson had ended his report with conclusions that were somewhat of a whimper:

> "Where the trade is great and nearly uniform, as is the case between Liverpool and Manchester, the expense of the Stationary system approximates probably more nearly to that of the Locomotive than in any other locality in England. It is in this instance, therefore, that despatch and public accommodation claim particular attention."

He would have been well aware of the brush his father had with the establishment, and he was after all only recently returned from his South American adventure. Better perhaps, having put before the directors of the Liverpool and Manchester Railway and his father's allies all the information they needed, for him to end on a diplomatic note.

Timothy Young rooted through the letters that cousin Sam Holmes had told him about, finding the one of 17th March, 1829 from Robert Stephenson to his grandfather, written just 10 days after Walker's report was delivered:

> My dear Sir
> The reports of the Engineers who visited the North to ascertain the relative merits of the two systems of Steam machinery now employed on Railways, have come to conclusions in favour of Stationary Engines. They have increased the performance of Fixed Engines beyond what practice will bear out, and I regret to say they have depreciated the Locomotive Engines below what experience has taught us... I write now to obtain answers to some questions, on which I think they have not given full information. Some of their calculations are also at variance with experiments that have come under your daily observation.
>
> ... will you be kind enough to state at what speed your own engine returns from Stockton with a given number of empty wagons and the rates of ascent. What load including wagons will an Engine weighing 9 tons including water take at the rate of 10 miles per hour – the speed to be maintained 20 or 30 miles without stopping? Let me have your general

opinion as to the Locomotive Engine System; is it as convenient as any other you have witnessed? Would you consider 13 1/2 tons in Summer and 10 tons in winter a fair performance for a good Locomotive Engine?

You will oblige me by answering as promptly as possible as the discussion on the merits of the two systems is yet going on amongst the directors here.

Direct to me, Railway Office Liverpool and believe me yours truly

Rob Stephenson

There was no indication as to how Robert Stephenson's report was received, except that he had turned to Timothy Hackworth for the views and judgement of a man at the front end of operations on the first public railway in England, no, in the world. The strongest simplest counter of all, based on experience that only came from actually running a public railway, was his grandfathers emphatic pronouncement in his response to the sense of desperation in Robert Stephenson's enquiry:

"Stationary Engines are by no means adapted to a public line of Railway... but you will fail in proving to the satisfaction of any one not conversant with these subjects, the inexpediency of such a system – it can never do for coaching – passengers cannot be accommodated – if endless ropes are used, there will be both danger, and delay. Who dare to be near when a mass of matter, standing at rest, say 20 to 30 tons, is first put in motion, by a rope moving at a rate of 10 to 15 miles, per hour. It need not be added what will follow? – a scene of endless confusion."

In the end, it was such a view from the Stockton and Darlington Railway that did confirm the conclusion the Stephensons, father and son, so sorely wanted. Besides condemning the stationary engine, Timothy Hackworth had cited the performance of Royal George. He also asserted his view that he was satisfied a locomotive engine of 10 horse power would convey 30 tons of goods in the winter, exclusive of the carriage, and 40 tons in summer. And that a laden Royal George frequently travelled at nine miles per hour. Further, his grandfather's words of wisdom, pointing to the future of the locomotive and its continuing development, could not have been more clearly stated:

> *"My general opinion, as to the L M System. I believe it is in a comparative state of infancy – swift engines upon a double way I am convinced may be used to the utmost advantage – improvements, upon anything yet produced of greater importance, in all respects, are clearly practicable, & I am sure this will prove itself, by actual remuneration to such parties as prudently yet diligently pursue the execution of this kind of power, with their eyes open to those alterations & advantages which actual demonstration of local circumstances point out."*

When Major Pangborn was shown the letter sent by Robert Stephenson he recognised and understood the caution of the directors of the Liverpool and Manchester Railway. Hetton Colliery had seen George Stephenson's locomotive withdrawn from a section for lack of power. Rumours, so often harbingers of bad news, about the affairs of the Stockton and Darlington Railway were also abroad– and the first year of running showed a bare break even. Moreover, it was the Newcastle to Carlisle Railway that had declined to include the use of the locomotive in its Bill that same year, 1829.

Timothy, though, had been more impressed with the straightforward and steadfast views expressed by his grandfather. He recognised it was practical experience that spoke out through years of work in actually making the Stockton and Darlington Railway a viable concern; Royal George was already capable of the performance that was required. Timothy Hackworth had been unequivocal – stationary engines and ropes would not work and the locomotive had yet more to offer in its development. Hidden away in the depths of the engineer's report was also an opinion, like that expressed by Robert Stephenson, which more readily sat on the fence, indeterminate as to whether it should be stationary engines or locomotives that should prevail. It offered the directors a different way forward to be considered, consistent, so as far as Timothy Hackworth was concerned, with the only practical approach. Something his grandson believed Major Pangborn should be made aware of.

'Robert said that the discussions were continuing among the directors. Look here at what Walker had written.' Timothy Young read the text he had marked out on page thirty-four, towards the end of Walker's report. "If any circumstances should induce you to proceed by degrees, and to proportion the power of conveyance to demand, then we recommend locomotive engines upon the line generally". Looking at Major Pangborn, who remained reading and by now having turned to and examining the reply from Timothy Hackworth, he continued. 'Added to the opinion given by my grandfather, that alternative would have led to further debate and charged discussion among the directors. For the supporters of Stephenson it re-opened the debate again. For the opponents of George Stephenson here was a single view of two independent-minded outsiders, not one, which they could not ignore.'

The directors met to make a final decision less than two weeks after the date of the reply to Robert Stephenson from Timothy Hackworth. It took one of the directors to put forward the proposition that won the day. There was one point on which Timothy Hackworth was emphatic and Walker and Rastrick, however much they favoured the use of stationary engines, were in accord; were the locomotive to be used, there was the possibility, over time, of continuing improvements in the power and performance of the locomotive. And Walker and Rastrick had actually gone one step further in their advice in such circumstances:

"...to enable you to take advantage of the improvements which may be made; with a view to encourage which, and to draw the attention of Engine-makers to the subject, something in the way of a premium, or an assurance of preference, might be held out to the person whose Engine was, upon experience, found to answer the best."

One of the directors, Richard Harrison, suggested that they did not need to wait for time to pass, that they should seek out and encourage the development of the locomotive, now. He proposed they offer a premium, just as Walker and Rastrick had suggested, for the development of a locomotive to suit their needs, but to do that before the line was opened. To run a competition that would establish whether a locomotive could be devised that was much improved and had the power. The winner, the locomotive found to answer the best, to be the one they adopted.

Major Pangborn had known there had been dissent, uncertainty, debate and disquiet about claims made for the early locomotives and that it resulted in a world famous trial of locomotive power. The content of the letters explained how the engineers preference had been set aside. It had also placed Timothy Hackworth at the centre of the debate about the way forward and, with his locomotive Royal George, tipped the scales in favour of the locomotive.

The arguing had been put to an end. The prospect of a competition satisfied both camps; those for George Stephenson and the locomotive and those lined up against him. For the doubters, there had been nothing to lose by following the advice of the engineers. Should it not be possible for a locomotive to be designed, constructed and tested to meet the required standards of the Liverpool and Manchester Railway, the use of stationary engines would be the settled solution.

Some things, Major Pangborn reflected, are far easier said than done. Since the scientific understanding of steam locomotion and the underlying mechanical engineering were in their infancy, deciding how to determine that a locomotive did indeed answer best for use on the line between Manchester and Liverpool was no straightforward matter in 1829. The terms that were settled on were complicated, intended to be realistic and the trial was to be held on part of the Liverpool to Manchester line, on a level stretch at Rainhill. The terms were published in the newspapers, and the competition was made open to any and all locomotive engineers. Amongst whom were George Stephenson, Robert Stephenson and Henry Booth, with more at stake and risk than any of the others. The trial at Rainhill was there for the winning. And winning would be everything.

CHAPTER THIRTEEN

It started with 'Royal George'

Exposition site, Friday 7th April 1893

Timothy Young tried to put himself in his grandfather's shoes. Difficult to imagine operating in the same world as the early pioneers – a world where there was as yet no dependable science or certainty about how to construct locomotives, and certainly not efficient locomotives; the only certainty about life in the collieries was the threat of explosion and of death. The scientists believed that the power of the locomotive was directly related to the size, to the weight, to the coal consumed. All too well known to the practitioners was the effect of breakdowns, of broken wheels, of wet and iced rails, of the push back from stormy and windy weather. As was the struggle to keep the locomotives in repair, even though there were only five of them on the Stockton and Darlington Railway, given that the workshops had to work with the most primitive of tools and equipment.

His grandfather was the one on whose shoulders it fell to make good on all those shortcomings, and he had no one else but himself to turn to when contemplating the difficulties, the deficiencies and the way forward. George Stephenson was completely taken over with resolving the difficulties of building the Liverpool and Manchester Railway. His son, Robert, was away in South America. That left only a caretaker manager in charge of the Newcastle works of Robert Stephenson and Co where the locomotives for the Stockton and Darlington Railway were built. If they were all feeling their way into this brave new world of locomotive steam power, his grandfather must have been feeling it most of all. There was no one else with responsibility for the operational side of a functioning railway, or another mind with an engineering bent to turn to. The Stockton and Darlington Railway was, after all, the only one like it in the world. He knew his grandfather's watchwords were simplicity and efficiency and Timothy Hackworth would be the one who applied those considerations as he wrestled with the deficiencies and looked for ways to improve.

Presumably, his grandson thought, based on his experience of repairing the locomotives supplied by Robert Stephenson and Company, he would have come to a settled view of what was required. He had apparently intimated as much. At the crucial meeting of the directors of the railway, one charged with deciding whether to turn the locomotives off the line and revert to the use of animal horsepower, he was asked his opinion as to which course of action should be followed. Without bravado or bluster his simple response was – "Gentlemen, if you allow me to make you an engine in my own way, I will engage that it shall answer your purpose."

Indeed, all the records showed that what he accomplished through his locomotive Royal George did meet their purpose, that of turning their railway into a viable financial enterprise. The turnaround was emphatic. Horses had shown themselves cheaper than the locomotives over the first eighteen months the railway was opened. Then, with Royal George, the running costs in its first year of working were half the costs of horse power; £466 as compared to £998, and Royal George, without the customary difficulties and setbacks, profitably carried more than 22,000 tons of goods; the share price, which had declined to £50 from its face value of £100, would show a threefold increase over the ensuing years.

To accomplish such a change in the fortunes of the locomotive, he would have needed to work out how to provide a locomotive with significantly more power. Timothy Young found what he needed in "Practical Mechanics Journal", a clear  account of the far-reaching changes his grandfather made to the locomotive:

There was an image of the locomotive and there was a sketch of the U-shaped return flue. That would have given a much larger heating surface than the simple single circular tube carried through the length of Stephenson's locomotives. But, such an increase in area meant he would have had to compensate in some way for the increase in weight of the locomotive that came about because of it. The drawing of the locomotive showed the boiler standing on six wheels, rather than Stephenson's standard of four. That would do two things. It would hold the load resting on the line to the same level as currently, so no further stress or level of rail breakages. It would also reduce slippage and wheel spinning under load by adding more adhesion through the number of increased contact points on the rail and give a stability and consistency of power delivery across a less than perfect railway line. Finally, there was not a single driver wheel to which the force of the pistons was transferred. The wheels were shown as being coupled, giving a forward motive force through each wheel.

The increased heating area, though, would have required a much improved heating force to be effective. Timothy Hackworth would have looked to draw on every ounce of power he could to generate the steam. He would definitely have wanted to increase the excitement of the coals.

Any smith would tell you that a strong blast of air through the coals of a forge was needed to increase the intensity, and thereby raise the temperature it could give to a piece of metal. And the force of that blast was accomplished by reducing the size of the outlet from the bellows, the source of the air. It would have taken him to see in his imagination, or maybe in a drawing, that the flow of steam into the chimney was sufficiently similar, that that was where the outflow would be – and deciding to constrict the flow there to create a blast through a single outlet would be the best option. Delivering an improved evaporative force to take advantage of the increased area of metal was what Timothy Young knew had been needed, and his grandfather had brought it into play. It would have moved his locomotive into another class. Timothy Young checked with the text that went with the article. Royal George was a triumph, certainly as far as a report

in the *The Engineer* by William Gowland, one of the men
who drove it, was concerned.

304	THE ENGINEER	OCT. 23, 1857

The true history of the thing is this:- I was driver of the "Royal George" on the
Stockton and Darlington Railway for about two years, it having come out of the Shildon
works in 1827 – the complete production of Mr. Timothy Hackworth. Its very first
journey proved its superiority in point of draught and production of steam. I was an
envied man, in consequence of the comfort I had through this mighty improvement.

At this moment is sitting beside me Mr. Robert Morrow, who remembers the
circumstances as well as I do myself. He was then driver of No. 2 on the same line –
one of Stephenson's make – and he had the offer of the "Royal George" but he did not
accept it; thinking, as he says, "that although his engine was not what he would like, he
preferred 'a bird in the hand to one in the bush'".

After the trial of the "Royal George", it so far surpassed everything which had come
from Newcastle, that Robert regretted sadly that he had not taken it, and the
remembrance of the cause of its superiority is strong in our memories to this day.

Bolton, October 19th   ------------   WILLIAM GOWLAND

The record that Rastrick and Walker had made of its
performance years earlier bore out that judgment. They
had contrasted the fuel consumption of Royal George
with other contemporary locomotives. Their report
cited the fuel used by Royal George in pounds per ton
of goods hauled – which they referenced as Locomotive
No 5 – as compared with the 2.16 lbs per ton average
for the Stephenson locomotives. Robert Stephenson had
also provided them with results from the experiment he
conducted with Royal George, when it ran in excess of 10
miles per hour under load, consuming 1.60 lbs per ton of
goods.

The consumption of the coals in the various locomotives
was a keenly felt criterion for Walker and Rastrick, relating
as it would to the economy of running locomotives. It was,
though, because their fuel consumption was considerably

more than the stationary engines in use at the time. The important criteria, now well understood by locomotive engineers at large, was how the power was produced. Power shows, but it's not through fuel consumption. Power generated was down to 'evaporative force' – how strong and constant a supply of steam at pressure could be produced. When Timothy Young looked, the efficiency of Royal George stood out by its lower consumption of fuel in the table Robert Stephenson had in his report, but its real power would show if it had hauled significantly heavier loads.

William Gowland had said he was a man to be envied and the records confirmed why that was so. Among the work records of Timothy Hackworth's locomotive drivers the truth of what his grandfather had accomplished stood out:

William Gowland: Days worked 269
Tons carried   1 mile/day 1,264   Average load 75.4

Robert Morrow: Days worked 271
Tons carried   1 mile/day 1,012   Average load 56 13

Royal George proved itself more powerful than the other locomotives every day. Twenty five per cent more powerful. It was a power to deliver from the extra heating surface combined with the high temperature of the coals that made his grandfather's locomotive stand out, and stand up to the constant rigours of hauling loads along the railway. How effective that had been was all too clear in Timothy Hackworth's letter. And from the results that Robert Stephenson obtained in the trial he made for them of his locomotive.

Sam Holmes had passed to him several letters his uncle had sent out to various engineering publications. And to the papers... When he read through them he found that often they were correcting errors in how Timothy Hackworth's work and contribution to the development of the locomotive ws being portrayed.

His Uncle John's account from his own experience of the development of Royal George set one in particular apart. It had a very particular explanation about the use of the exhaust steam, and the construction of what would be called the 'blast-pipe.

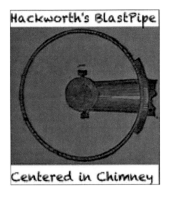

Hackworth's BlastPipe

Centered in Chimney

Constricted at Top
of Steam exhaust

The constriction of the opening at the top, the orifice of the single eduction pipe introduced into the chimney, was described as being "accomplished by a coned piece of malleable iron pipe, shrunk and pinned on to the blast-pipe." This letter to *The Engineer* also went on to describe how Timothy Hackworth made the fullest use of the steam in driving fresh new power into his locomotive:

"Royal George" had the blast pipe; and not only so, but, to make a certainty doubly sure, the inventor accompanied its first adoption with an auxiliary pipe leading from the main eduction pipe previous to its entering the chimney - this could be used or not, at the pleasure of the driver - and discharged its jet beneath the grate bars, to aid combustion. I was with the "Royal George" the first Stockton trip she made, and well remember laying down in the tender to look at the effect of the discharge-pipe below the fire-grate. There was also another use made of the exhaust steam, viz., to heat the feed water; the supply (as in the previous instance) was under control of the driver. Now, to entertain the idea that this threefold application is all to be ascribed to the chapter of accidents, would be an outrage on common sense."

Taking the steam outlet from both cylinders into just one pipe, centering it in the chimney and constricting the outlet orifice would tie in with what a smith knew of raising a sufficiently hot fire for the work in hand... A quite deliberate constriction of the steam outlet to create a force of air that would raise the temperature and also significantly increase the evaporative power. But Timothy Hackworth had evidently, when he applied it to the locomotive, taken that already inventive idea one step forward. What could have been more simple than making the steam work again after it had driven the pistons, using it in three ways to ensure the consistent delivery of power. The draught of air was forcibly increased, the water going to the boiler could be preheated and, should it be needed, an additional jet of steam could be used directly under the firegrate. There was going to be no shortfall in the evaporative force that would drive Royal George.

What his grandfather had done was to simultaneously increase, no double, the heating surface and, making full use of the steam, turn that potential to deliver increased power into a reality. Placing it on six wheels gave the additional traction to deliver the power to the rails, and removed the instability of a four wheel drive, with its history of slippage and an inclination to derail. Bringing that all together in one locomotive didn't come about through any incremental, piece-meal, stage by stage improvements; it was a leap forward. A leap forward through the ingenuity of Timothy Hackworth – yes maybe even a 'sagacity' that came from a combination of experience and skill that marked him out as a locomotive engineer 'extraordinaire'. In practical terms Royal George changed the finances of the Stockton and Darlington Railway, and changed the face of locomotive performance.

The words of Walker and Rastrick, if they were to be believed, had put his grandfather's work in a class of its own. "Hackworth's engine is undoubtedly the most powerful that has yet been made, as the amount of tons conveyed by it, compared with other engines proves." Now Timothy Young understood the justice of those words and their importance.

Robert Stephenson, if only he had taken Timothy Hackworth along with him as a dependable witness, had figures from the performance of Royal George that met the requirements of the Liverpool and Manchester Railway. He'd recorded a loaded Royal George achieving 11 miles and hour over a distance of three miles, and at no time running out of steam. Beyond that the records from the Stockton and Darlington Railway were already enough on their own. His grandfather's locomotive hadn't hauled less than 40 tons of goods at a speed that was held back to 5 miles per hour; the speed decreed as a maximum by the directors of the Stockton and Darlington Railway. On the basis of that experience alone, Hackworth's projections as to what could be accomplished were several times more than that assumed by Walker and Rastrick in their calculations. And according to engineer, Zerah Colborn, Royal George was capable of hauling a load at nine miles an hour, even to a maximum of thirty-two loaded wagons.

He looked again at the figures. William Gowland carried the equivalent of 1200 tons a mile each day. That would translate into 60 Royal Georges that would be needed to haul the anticipated quantity of goods the 30-mile journey to Liverpool and back each day. And, if fitted with driving wheels of five-foot diameter, as Walker and Rastrick assumed the locomotives on the Manchester and Liverpool Railway would be, the performance of Royal George would be boosted by a corresponding further 20 per cent increase in speed.

He went back to the engineers report. They had based their financial projections on over 100 locomotives being needed, adding £35,000, or an additional two-thirds, to capital requirements and increasing running costs by more than £15,000. The estimates they offered were too pessimistic. Timothy Hackworth's practical results had proved them wrong. A reflection of his grandfather's prowess. The case for the locomotive should have been cast iron. A mirror image of arrangements that worked so profitably for the Stockton and Darlington Railway would have served just as well for what was planned for the Liverpool and Manchester Railway.

Timothy Hackworth Young, as Major Pangborn hoped, had brought to the light of day the significance of his grandfather's work and Royal George. The locomotive was designed by his grandfather, was built under his direction, was constructed to his standards, was used to haul the Stockton and Darlington Railway back into the black, was sufficient to forestall the possibility of the locomotive being turned off the line altogether. He literally had pulled iron out of the fire and made something of the locomotive.

Major Pangborn had been right, and Timothy Young grasped exactly why he had wanted to bring that locomotive, of all locomotives, to the fore. Royal George had been a milestone event. Something his grandfather's inventiveness created; a spirit that lasted for years and impacted the way the railway he worked for would develop. Telling the public the story of the place Royal George had in the history of the Stockton and Darlington Railway would be the starting point for a display of the work of the pioneers in the Inventors Gallery.

There was not a better or a more original mind than that of Timothy Hackworth. He looked at the evidence in front of him: the engineering journals, the workshop records, and the letters. He might originally have been concerned as to how Major Pangborn was going to bring the story of his grandfather to a wide audience. Not now... He was a locomotive man, here to tell a story and proud to have come from Hackworth stock. His grandfather's locomotives would stand as testament to his abilities and contribution

The quotation from Samuel Smiles book came to mind: "The true founder of the railway system was the man who invented such a locomotive as made railway locomotion practicable and profitable." He gathered together all that he had to hand. Time to talk with Major Pangborn. Time for letting what he now knew of his grandfather's work speak for itself; time for Royal George to show its colours.

CHAPTER FOURTEEN

Taking on the challenge – may the best man win!

Exposition site, Saturday 8th April 1893

Major Pangborn had been impressed, although Timothy couldn't tell whether the ebullient smile that had spread across his face was intended for him or reflected a touch of self-congratulation. It didn't matter. What mattered was getting the endorsement of the man who brought him to the Exposition to complete one task in particular, that of bringing his grandfather's accomplishments to the fore. All that he put forward was received with suitable nods of the head in affirmation, and an occasional muted 'Mmm' as recognition of his diligence.

Superintendent Timothy Young had made a job of it. Royal George would, as Pangborn had hoped, stand out; stand first in line alongside the first of the portraits in the Inventors gallery. The puzzle was how his grandfather Timothy Hackworth, with such a head start, failed to capitalise on his engineering prowess when it came to competing with George Stephenson. Time to open that Pandora's Box after they had had lunch and could return to it suitably refuelled.

The two men walked down the steps from the Administration Building, heading for the simple restaurant in the Terminal Station. There could be no better statement of the intention of the city of Chicago to create a lasting impression in the mind of visitors than the huge Statue of the Republic directly ahead of them. Like the Colossus of Rhodes it stood tall above its watery surroundings, its size dwarfing everything around it. The orb surmounted by an eagle was held aloft, and the staff with the snake curled around its shaft, reached up to the skies above. The plinth rising from the water was as large as the arch supporting the sculpture, which itself was a tribute to Columbus. The statues gracing each of the colonnades of the buildings that flanked the lagoon appeared as midgets. The gilding shone too brightly to be ignored. It was the centrepiece and the boats plying across the lagoon, pausing in their journey, would ensure visitors were held in awe of its majesty.

'Your job was to discover and impress just as much as this does,' said the Major, pointing at the statue towering above them. 'Well you have definitely put us on the right track. But then someone from Hackworth stock would, wouldn't he? It's obviously in your blood.' He paused. 'I'll report back to Charles Lord as to how much progress we have made. He ought to tell your Mr Layton what a good job you have done. You are credit to the Milwaukee Road Railway.'

Timothy Young was more concerned with what had still to be said about his grandfather. 'This isn't finished yet. You said before that Hackworth and Stephenson suffered setbacks... and the notice alongside Sanspareil said my grandfather's locomotive had failed at the Rainhill Trials.

I don't see how that could have happened...' Before he could complete that thought, Major Pangborn interrupted. 'Plenty of time for that during this afternoon.' A pause while he considered what else he had to do. 'Before I take my walk-round to make sure all is well with the major exhibitors. I have to keep in with all that is modern. Our world is changing at a fast pace. Better to be on the train of progress than running fast behind it to try and keep up, not get left behind. Staying at the front, reporting for the front page. That's always the name of the game.'

'Well that's exactly where grandfather was left after Royal George was put to the line,' Timothy replied. 'Now I need to pick up what happened with the trial for the railway that George Stephenson carved out and how he came to be in front.'

'Come on, Timothy. Lets get to food first. Then back to my office.'

Major Pangborn always worked better after a meal and when he was no longer hungry. The fare in the Terminus Restaurant had been simple but filling, and he'd made his number with Mary, one of the waitresses, making sure he got favoured treatment. As he should, he thought. He returned to his office in the Administration Building a contented man. Time to set his aide to work.

He looked across at Timothy Young, thought for a moment about the Rainhill Trials and what material he could best handover, then found and placed out on his desk the 1830 edition of Arcana of Science and Art. Best offer a brief introduction, sufficient that his superintendent could piece together events and add any family recollections.

'Rainhill. The Trial. The eyes of the world were on iron horses racing across a single mile of track. Calamity for your grandfather. Over four days George Stephenson and Rocket won out. Claimed the prize of building the locomotives for the railway between Liverpool to Manchester.'

Timothy eyed the front page with its drawings of the contenders, reached out, brought it to his side of Major Pangborn's desk and flicked through the first few pages. Day by day there was an account of the event. 'I thought Rainhill was just a straight race between the contenders.'

'No. It was set for each contender to run the equivalent of the thirty miles at full speed, with load, and against the clock. Backwards and forwards each contender went to complete the distance, stopping to take on fuel and water at each turn as they needed. Three judges to see it was played by the rules. Two of whom were responsible for the timings across the mile posts; Rastrick one of the engineers who had produced the report for the directors, and Nicholas Wood from Killingworth with all the practical experience he could bring to the event.'

'Killingworth. Wasn't that George Stephenson's home territory? He wouldn't be at all partisan would he?' was Timothy's caustic observation.

'Well he was certainly a fan of George Stephenson. Not the only one. And he'd had Robert Stephenson as his apprentice for a while before Robert went to South America. Oh, and he'd made the track at Killingworth available for Robert to conduct his trials of Rocket while it was under construction.'

'Quite. Given them a bit of a head start over the rest of the field. Did everyone get a chance to prove their locomotives before the trials began?'

'Well I guess they did. Remember there were no railways to get the locomotives to Rainhill. They were all brought in bits, by sea and overland by coach, re-assembled and the first day of the trial was much of a proving demonstration of their working.'

Timothy Young could see there were reports of more than three entrants. All his preconceptions about the trial would have to be set aside. 'The trial started out with five contenders?'

Major Pangborn had been told about the original flurry of entrants the competition flushed out; wild and woolly ideas from across the land. One of the more plausible ones had taken the notion of using only the minimal horse power to the very edge. Cycloped was a horse on a carriage with a perpetual roller on which it was supposed to canter, thereby driving the wheels below. Put to the test it turned out to be as ill-thought out as it was ill-conceived. There were as many who wanted the locomotive to fail as there were those who willed it to succeed. They were not disappointed. The whole thing collapsed in a heap, the horse shaking itself free, running amok; much to the laughter of the crowds watching from the stands.

That first showing of the locomotives made it plain there were only three serious contenders: Novelty the sprinting favourite, Sanspareil with a serious turn of speed for its size and Rocket which, driven by George Stephenson, had already brought the directors of the Liverpool and Manchester Railway up to the site. That man didn't miss a trick, Major Pangborn thought to himself. You had to admire the sheer opportunism and showmanship of George Stephenson.

He briefly responded to the question from Timothy. 'Those numbers were soon whittled down. Each of the final contenders was allocated a day for their trial. George Stephenson pushed himself to the front of the queue, egged on by ambition and determination. There's always something about making a first impression. He might have had the directors in the palm of his hand but he wanted to hold the popular vote too. Take a careful look. Each day is set out in detail. Including the failure of Sanspareil. And here are the copies I made directly from Rastrick's notebook of the timings for runs.'

Timothy was left with a distinctly quizzical look on his face. He had not only been given food to digest at lunchtime; here he was handed food for thought. Figures from an engineer's records was a source he would be content to rely on, much rather that than the anecdotal news from the press and the reportings in engineering journals alone. Cousin Sam and Aunt Pru had made him well aware of the difficulties Timothy Hackworth laboured under in building a locomotive to compete in the trials but, and it was a big but, the sagacity credited to his grandfather would surely not have let him down. After all it was his judgment so clearly expressed in his letter to Robert Stephenson that the locomotive development called for by the Liverpool and Manchester Railway was well within grasp.

Major Pangborn had once again set the scene, interested to see what view a locomotive man might take of the events at Rainhill. Meanwhile, he had other business to attend to. He'd heard a rumour that the New York Central Railroad were putting to the line a fast passenger locomotive that would break all records for speed. If it did, and if he could put it on display here for the duration of the Exposition, that would be a visitor attraction beyond all others to pull in the crowds to the full sweep of the Baltimore and Ohio Railroad exhibit he'd created. The display in the Transportation Annex already included the first American locomotive in the state of New York. Putting the latest and the fastest on show next to it would be a coup, and one that he could make sure would grab newspaper headlines. He gently ushered Superintendent Timothy Young out of his office and on his way.

Readying for the task at hand, Timothy moved his working papers on his rolltop desk to one side. All the locomotive displays in the annex were in place. He'd never had so many locomotives under his control. These locomotives only had to look good. None of the lengthy work to check boilers, tubes or wheels that was called for after hours of running under steam. He ought to go on his afternoon inspection, but it would need little of his time. The schedules of cleaning, polishing and inspection of all the locomotive exhibits were well underway. Instead he made himself as comfortable as he could in his chair and placed his hands on the desk top in front of himself. Major Pangborn had been more than satisfied with what he had found about Royal George. Time now to contemplate the next chapter in his grandfather's development of the locomotive. Supposedly, according to the Major, events had come crashing round his grandfather's head this time. Stephenson, having survived his own baptism of fire, was set to capture the prize.

The news reports set out the events of the days of the trial. No difficulty getting thousands of visitors to see the spectacle. Some difficulty in working out the conditions, and they were changed over the course of the first days. Allowance was made for different competitors; locomotives on six wheels, locomotives on four, locomotives of different weights. And those of least weight were favoured so that, while the distance for the trial was set as being about the same as the run from Liverpool to Manchester, the load to be hauled was varied. Timothy Hackworth Young was left scratching his head at the possibilities. The original idea had been to establish locomotives capable of hauling loads of 20 tons at 10 miles per hour. He wasn't sure who had decided to change that requirement to three times the locomotive's weight, as though lighter engines would somehow be hauling lesser loads in practice. Of course they would need less power to get going, to overcome the inertia of the engine, but they would still have to haul a full load if the Liverpool and Manchester Railway were going to seize the sizable amount of the canal traffic that had been promised. It was all a puzzle to Timothy Hackworth Young. And nowhere was any way described as to how any decision would be made as to which entrant had won. Or who would reach that momentous decision. To judge from Rastrick's comments that Major Pangborn had noted, there would be no account taken of theirs, the engineers', view. They were only timekeepers.

The outcome was however unambiguous. Although the others put in credible performances as to what the locomotive was capable of achieving, Rocket was last man standing...the only locomotive to complete the trial.

Timothy Young buried himself in the day-by-day reports of what had happened at Rainhill between October the sixth and the fourteenth in 1829. First day of the trial itself, the main contenders had shown their paces in front of the gathered audience. Rocket was let loose, clearly met the stipulated speed for the competition, and even ran at nearly 20 mph without load, a speed not seen before. Novelty though looked completely different to any other locomotive design, and its light frame without load positively darted past spectators at an even greater speed, just short of 30 miles an hour. Sanspareil too showed its paces, leading to the comment "It was soon manifest that a powerful competitor has entered the field". The second day Novelty, tried under load, exceeded the performance of Rocket. George Stephenson evidently had a serious competition on his hands.

Novelty was the lightweight locomotive that he and his son hadn't allowed for. It also had no separate tender with the fuel and water. It was self-contained. So there were grounds for the calculation of the load to be hauled to be revised, calculated on the basis of including the weight of the tender, fuel and water as part of the load. Alterations that the three judges put their names to, and were carefully dated back to October 6, the published start date of the trials. It was agreed other new conditions should apply and so day three became the first trial run proper.

Timothy noted one particular change they made. It was to the regulation of the acceptable steam pressure. The original stipulations were in two parts. Firstly, he surmised for consideration of operational safety, that the boiler of each entrant should be tested up to 150 psi and with an intended limit of 60 psi on the pressure valve, at which point it should 'blow off' the excess pressure. Secondly that the operating steam pressure would be no more than 50 pounds per square inch. The alteration was subtle but definite and to Stephenson's advantage given the more robust construction of Rocket. The new pressure stipulation was that it would be 50 psi only at starting. There was no other constraint specified. From experience he knew that was just the uplift in performance that a locomotive driver would be tempted into exploiting – running up to 60 psi would gain an extra 20%. And there had been no mention of ascertaining whether the intended upper limit on the pressure had been increased as well. He would see how the results for Rocket had turned out.

The final running order became: Oct 6, demonstration runs; Oct 7, Novelty first trial run. Rain and mud on the track stopped play; Oct 8, revised 'Stipulations and Conditions', Rocket trial runs; Oct 10, Novelty in need of repair, George Stephenson demonstration runs with Rocket, Novelty demonstration runs after repair. Matched for speed. Then it was time for Sanspareil to be put through its paces.

Timothy Hackworth had been at Rainhill since the start of the trials. He assembled and had rebuilt Sanspareil after its journey by sea and land, shown its capabilities on the first day and would have noted the change in the stipulations for the trial. Cousin Sam and Aunt Pru had described the difficult conditions he had laboured under in making the locomotive, and how he was beholden to Robert Stephenson and Co for the cylinders and to Michael Longridge's Bedlington Iron Works for the boiler, the latter for which he had much caulking to do to make the cylinder steam tight. The delays took his trial run to the Sunday, and he requested that it be deferred until the Monday, which was when calamity struck.

Monday Oct 13, Day 6. Sanspareil trial. His grandfather's locomotive ran for two hours until a cylinder gave way and it could then no longer continue. He was denied any opportunity of time to repair the faults, and for him the competition was over. The details on the placard Major Pangborn had set alongside the Sanspareil for the Exposition were right – events beyond his grandfather's control had come crashing round his head. Even so he had given his help to a fellow locomotive engineer in repairing Novelty. He read on...

Tuesday Oct 14, Day 7. Novelty trial under the new conditions.

That locomotive too failed again, even though it was working at 15 mph over the first two trips, when the cement on the flanges failed. The joints were determined too green and not set so that Braithwaite and Ericsson declined to continue, requesting that their entry be judged on the results recorded thus far. George Stephenson's instinct had served him well. Lightweight Novelty wasn't up to a heavyweight task.

Timothy Young carefully checked over the reports in front of him. As far as he could see no allowance was made for either Novelty or Sanspareil not having had the advantage of the Stephenson's in carrying out proving trials, an opportunity to iron out any defects. Although they put in credible demonstration as to what a locomotive was capable of achieving, their results did not stand. Advantage was well and truly taken by the home side.

George Stephenson had made sure the world at large, the visitors gathered from around the world, the doubting engineers, the merchants, the owners of the canals, the shareholders and the directors of Liverpool and Manchester Railway had seen a spectacle to behold. He had run first, making sure he was the one who had made a first impression. He carried the livery and style of the stagecoach to signal who it was that he was about to put in the shade for speed. He had opened up the experience for the crowds and been the first to show a locomotive, his locomotive Rocket, carrying passengers. When Novelty failed he'd stepped in and with his locomotive stripped down to racing trim had shown Rocket successfully running up and down the track at a speed to match any competitor. He found speeds that far exceeded the standard that engineers and directors of the railway, for which he was superintendent, had called for. Speeds that justified the claims he had made about the potential of the locomotive. He put the doubters to shame. He let his son put the final nail in the coffin of any consideration of the need for any stationary steam engines between Liverpool and Manchester. He allowed him to put on a series of demonstrations of Rocket running up the incline at Rainhill at 15 miles per hour, hauling a carriage filled with passengers. A demonstration he permitted to be carried out in the morning after Sanspareil had its trial, giving the clear impression of Rocket standing head and shoulders above his experienced rival. Whatever had to be done, Timothy Young realised all too well, George Stephenson had got there first.

The outcome of the Rainhill Trials was unambiguous. While Novelty had shown off the speed possible from a smaller locomotive and Sanspareil had shown the power that could be delivered by a locomotive less than half the weight of Royal George, Rocket was awarded the prize as the locomotive left standing...the only locomotive to complete the trial. And to drive the point home, George Stephenson brought Rocket back to the track and ran it at full speed. It was recorded as travelling at 35 miles per hour. He had run the opposition into the ground.

It was George Stephenson who had devised a locomotive that ran on four wheels, reduced the load and weight on the track and which, as Timothy Young recognised, incorporated a revolutionary boiler with the potential to deliver more power than ever before. A multi-tubular boiler.... And the directors immediately after the trial came off the fence, committed themselves and their enterprise to the use of locomotive power, placed orders with Robert Stephenson and Co for six such locomotives for the Liverpool and Manchester Railway.

Nothing though so far had adequately explained for Timothy how it was his grandfather had not fulfilled his own expectations or met the requirements of the Manchester railway. Which was the frame of mind that Major Pangborn later found him in when he returned from his meeting and conversations elsewhere, pleased with his own progress and curious to find out what more had been established by his Superintendent.

'Timothy. You won't believe what I have just seen. The most astonishing contrivance. I was dealing with the arrangements for the locomotive speed merchant from New York to be included with our displays when someone suggested I shouldn't get too excited. There was a locomotive exhibit already on the Midway that would leave visitors speechless. I assumed they were referring to the Ice Locomotive. That glorious rollercoaster ride that has been fitted out to run over ice frozen onto the rails. No. It was a locomotive driven by massive hydraulic force skidding over a layer of water on rails. Engineering nightmare so I was told. Supposedly going to travel even faster than locomotive 999. Do you know what? No contest. We're sticking with the pride of New York – that could be 100 miles an hour, done, dusted and proven in operation. Now that's progress in action.'

Timothy Young looked up and into the inevitably enthusiastic smiling face of Major Pangborn. The man was indomitable. 'What progress with your story of Rainhill?'

Certainly not the progress Timothy had wanted to make. He'd seen up far too close the events that had led to his grandfather's efforts falling by the wayside.

'It looked like George Stephenson had the field to himself. Regardless of what the plans for the trial had been he tore up any rule book there was. He made two early runs with Rocket, then two demonstration runs, then the actual trial, then another run when Novelty failed, then a run up an incline and finally another run at the end of the competition.'

Major Pangborn listened attentively. There was no doubt that Novelty had been the crowds favourite; a crowd whose greatest experience of speed before was seeing a horse racing at full gallop and the thud on the earth as it passed by. Novelty had, in the words of one reporter, 'skipped by', light on its feet and easy on the eye. But then, when it was put to the test, it failed. Broke down, was repaired and then broke down again. Rocket had put in the full complement of runs so that it had worked to the same distance as a run between Manchester and Liverpool. He only knew that Rocket had been acclaimed at Rainhill and ever since. The master locomotive engineer from Shildon, this man's grandfather, had moved locomotive design forward after Rainhill but this competition had not been his finest hour. Sanspareil had made runs of the same duration as Rocket before failing. There had been no hiding the ignominious and spectacular end to the eighth run, occurring right in front of the stands. However well thought of he was at Shildon, the world at large had seen a lesser man here.

'Come along Mr Hackworth Young. Don't be so downcast. Rainhill was only part of one chapter in the locomotive coming of age. Your grandfather's Royal George gave the world and the locomotive its start.'

'But all Stephenson's showmanship didn't mean that Rocket was the best locomotive did it?' Timothy Young felt for his grandfather. He paused, letting that question fall between the two men. 'Or that Sanspareil should be ignored? You're all fired up about Locomotive Number 999, all because it may travel at 100 miles per hour. For how long? For how far? Speed isn't everything.'

The minute he had said those words Timothy realised what had been gnawing away at him as he had been over the events at Rainhill. Rocket recorded so many different speeds it was difficult to credit that it was the same locomotive each time.

'What was needed in a locomotive was consistency. The speed recorded for Rocket was in different runs at different times -10 miles an hour, 14 miles an hour, 18 miles an hour, 25 miles an hour, 28 miles an hour and 35 miles an hour. Results under trial conditions, results with no load, timings from runs carrying passengers.' He remained disconcerted but emphatic about what he was going to do. 'That all needs explaining before anyone can claim that Rocket was the best locomotive.' Timothy Young was determined to look at the records and the observations of engineers. He wouldn't be downcast for much longer.

Major Pangborn had regaled him with the arrangements he had been able to make to get Locomotive 999 to the Exposition – a homegrown wonder for the American public to take pride in and enjoy. For him that was enough accomplished for one day. Beyond that he was more than pleased to see the practiced experience of a locomotive man brought to discovering what he could about events at Rainhill.

'Well I'll leave that in your hands.'

Timothy settled back into the task he'd set himself. The figures from Rastrick's notebook – the engineer with a professional reputation to maintain – would tell their own story. Far more dependable to a locomotive man than partisan reports in the papers. Time for him to look over the results that were set out in the judge's notebook, every set of figures more dependable than a thousand different opinions. He opened the note book and looked across the pages of hand-written figures. Each run of each locomotive had been carefully recorded in a precise format, setting out columns for times at start, between the marker posts, and time spent between trips. According to the reports, George Stephenson had made sure his trial was run before the other contenders. Undertaken according to the new regulations. This was the first trial that would count, although it was the second timed trial that the public had witnessed.

The judges would then have had an idea as to how each locomotive was faring, fastest speed now rising comfortably above the minimum 10 miles per hour called for in the stipulations for the trial. A speed though that Rocket had only just exceeded two days previously. Timothy reckoned that, if he had been George Stephenson, he would have been keeping a keen eye on how the contenders performed, undoubtedly keeping informed by Nicholas Woods as timekeeper at the far end of the run.

The change in the way the weight was calculated meant the weight of the tender, three tons and four hundredweight, was then included as part of the load to be hauled. That effectively reduced the load for Rocket by a quarter compared to the weight it hauled on the run on the first day. Timothy Hackworth Young scanned down the columns of figures recorded in Rastrick's notebook, they showed Rocket then running at an improved average speed of 13 miles per hour for the trips of the first run, just as he expected from the changes that were made. But its performance varied between a best time of 11 minutes and 25 seconds for two trips between the marker posts, and a worst time of 18 minutes and 40 seconds, which probably explained the comment he'd read earlier that it "ran with considerable variation of velocity".

And of the trips of the second run, when he looked, they were around the 13 minutes mark.

Stephenson			Start time			
8th Oct Run2			2.03.12			

Time to Steam up	Time at Post1	Return Time P2-P1	Time Going P1-P2	Time at Post2	Time Stopped	Run Time
0.1.38	2.04.50		0.6.15	2.11.5	0.2.08	
	2.20.45	0.7.32		2.13.13		0.13.47
0.2.25	2.23.10		0.5.57	2.29.07	0.2.23	
	2.38.50	0.7.20		2.31.30		0.13.17
0.2.30	2.41.20		0.5.17	2.46.37	0.2.59	
	2.55.48	0.6.12		2.49.36		0.11.29
0.2.47	2.58.35		0.7.07	3.05.41	0.3.40	
	3.16.08	0.6.47		3.09.21		0.13.54

Rocket was running at nearly four miles an hour above the speed stipulated by the directors for the trial. The timings had improved over the previous run, increasing the average by anything up to a further 25 per cent, with one recorded giving a best top speed of 16 miles per hour. An improvement consistent with advantage being taken of the new higher level of pressure possible under the revised regulations. But had it been good enough to beat the performance Sanspareil was capable of?

The recorded timings of five days later showed that Sanspareil ran consistently backwards and forwards along the one and a half miles, with no extended delays at turn-round as recorded for Rocket. Timothy Hackworth's locomotive made a first trip at a speed that set all the others in the shade, even exceeding that recorded for Novelty in the trials.

Hackworth *13th Oct*				Start time 10.10.21		
Time to Steam up	Time at Post1	Return Time P2-P1	Time Going P1-P2	Time at Post2	Time Stopped	*Run Time*
0.1.09	10.11.30		0.5.09	10.16.39	0.2.06	
	10.26.22	0.7.37		10.18.45		0.12.46
0.2.12	10.28.34		0.6.03	10.34.37	0.2.01	
	10.43.46	0.7.8		10.36.38		0.13.11
0.2.11	10.45.57		0.6.08	10.52.05	0.2.11	
	11.01.37	0.7.21		10.54.10		0.13.29
0.2.35	11.04.12		0.5.34	11.09.46	0.1.52	
	11.18.12	0.6.34		11.11.38		0.12.08

Everyone could see from those results that a serious contender had entered the field. The recorded average speed for Sanspareil, across the seven trips it made, he calculated as more than 14 miles an hour.

Timothy Young looked to see what other practical men had made of Rainhill and the outcome. He turned to Zerah Colborn and his extensive account of 'History of the Locomotive Engine'. He had an engineers eye for detail which he gave to each of the contenders he described, concluding with *"The real power of the 'Sanspareil' is to be estimated by its rate of evaporation, which was one- third greater than that of the 'Rocket' and thus the 'Sanspareil,' after allowing for its greater weight, was the most powerful engine brought forward for trial. . . As far as it had gone, the mean rate of speed (of the 'Sanspareil') was greater than that of the 'Rocket' up to the same stage of the experiment."* He also translated the work that was accomplished into the Horse Power of each locomotive. Rocket he calculated as 12 Horse power, with Sanspareil rated at 18 Horse Power. And he made clear that the failure of the contenders to Rocket was acknowledged by one of the Rainhill judges as being of no reflection on them as *"performances of 'Rocket' were nevertheless surpassed by both these engines...and their final failure as Mr Wood has candidly recorded, did not arise from any defect in the principles upon which they were constructed."*

All this still left unexplained the additional speed that Rocket achieved when at the end of the trial and having been declared the winner, George Stephenson brought out Rocket for a victory lap. Until then, using all the wiles at his disposal, Rocket completely stripped down had reached 30 miles an hour. Now it was taken to 35 miles an hour, to put an emphatic stamp on its superiority and place the result beyond doubt. The locomotive man's mind of Superintendent Timothy Young was left filled with doubt. How was that speed achieved? Was it because he had run with a minimum load of water? Was it because he had used the driver's trick of tying down the safety valve and taken the steam pressure well above the limit? Or, since the stories abounded, was it because he discovered the secret of the blast-pipe and been able to introduce some aspect of its effect into Rocket? It probably was of little consequence as to how George Stephenson had managed to force that extra performance from Rocket. But... Showboating was one thing. Delivering power and how to live up to such promised performance from Stephenson's locomotives would be quite another.

In any event, the records confirmed that Sanspareil had run consistently and run faster than Rocket, even with the heavier load assigned to it. His grandfather's best endeavours had been beaten, not by Rocket but by careless work on the boiler and deficiencies in the casting of the cylinders. And through the introduction by others of new rules that were advantageous to the performance of Rocket. Rainhill had handed the Liverpool and Manchester Railway to George Stephenson on a plate. At the end of the trial, it was he who had it in the bag; orders for six locomotives had been placed.

His grandfather, Timothy Hackworth, had complied with the original conditions, had built a locomotive of considerably less weight than Royal George but still of substantial power – more than sufficient to haul the load on the Liverpool and Manchester Railway. He was refused the opportunity, given to Novelty, of repair – although strictly what was called for was no more than simple replacement of the failed cylinder. The results of which he was later able to report to the directors of the Liverpool and Manchester Railway. They relented but only to the extent of agreeing to purchase Sanspareil at the price set out in the original conditions. Less generous than the way in which Braithwaite and Ericson, owners of Novelty were treated. But it had not been too late for his grandfather to set the record straight. Among the family correspondence Sam Holmes had provided was a letter penned to the directors of the Liverpool and Manchester Railway after Rainhill that said it all. Timothy Hackworth would as always stake his reputation on his practical accomplishment.

Timothy Young had seen for himself, now understood and shared the family's frustration. Sanspareil in practice had them all beaten. But at Rainhill the best man didn't win and his grandfather's efforts were in vain. The die had been cast. Too late to change direction after that.

When his grandfather left the field of battle at Rainhill, Timothy thought he could maybe have taken encouragement from the words of non-conformist author John Bunyan. In 'Pilgrims Progress' he wrote of 'Christian' travelling through the 'Slough of Despond', putting on his armour from God and winning the battle. Now, his grandfather's inventiveness, experience and hard won skills would be brought to bear on the needs of the Stockton and Darlington Railway. Perhaps that was where it was intended that his talents should prevail.

Timothy Young, as his grandfather would have done, lifted his eyes to the hills. Next to the letter in the bundle Sam Holmes had sent was one that recorded events after Rainhill. It concerned the latest locomotive delivered to the Stockton and Darlington Railway by Robert Stephenson & Co. It had been tried whilst his grandfather was away at Rainhill. And it too was named by them 'Rocket'. Its behaviour was erratic, running away on its own, and it was nicknamed by the drivers 'Maniac'. Moreover it broke down. It didn't work. It fell to Timothy Hackworth to recover it from the track using Royal George and it spent more than a week in repairs to make good on a failed force pump and the hand gear and valves.

If this was the engineering standard the Stephensons were going to apply then the Liverpool and Manchester Railway would have their time cut out trying to run a railway. It would be an uphill struggle.

CHAPTER FIFTEEN

Losers and losses

Exposition site, Monday 10th April 1893

This Monday morning Major Pangborn looked forward to another good week. Another week nearer to the opening. The time by which the near empty walkways and the tracks and locomotives that stood in the huge extension of the Transportation Building would become awash with visitors as the crowds swept through. He and his Superintendent Timothy Hackworth Young had done well. The last of the arrangements had to be made about bringing the record holding Locomotive 999 to the site, and welcoming 'Samson', one of the last of the early locomotives and with it one of the last of the 'old school' drivers. All else about the locomotives on display was accomplished or sufficiently under control that they could be confident that it would be ready.

The display he planned for the Inventors Gallery was clear in his mind. The history of the locomotive in America and the part played by Matthew Baldwin, Horatio Allen and Ross Winans was a matter of established record. Now that the story of Royal George had been uncovered by Timothy Young, they could focus on portraying the part played by George Stephenson and Rocket for the Liverpool and Manchester Railway.

Even though Timothy had an account to give of his grandfather's locomotive Sanspareil, there was no reason to change or add to the wording on the plaque he had placed alongside the lifesize model he had had constructed.

Timothy Young had looked beyond Rainhill and had other ideas.

George Stephenson, from a suggestion made by Henry Booth the Secretary of the Liverpool and Manchester Railway, had moved boiler design on to an arrangement that still held good – the use of a multitude of tubes, rather than a single flue, as a way of heating the water and generating the quantity of steam needed to propel locomotives. It was, as Timothy Young was well aware, not as efficient as the direct heat from a single flue. The performance of Sanspareil was sufficient testament to that, as was what followed on from Rainhill. He'd found reference in both Colborn's book and in 'Arcana of Science' to alterations being made to Rocket, considerable alterations if the report was to be believed.

Indeed there had been. Engineering Rocket in the first place would have been an extraordinary challenge compared to anything George Stephenson or Robert Stephenson & Co had built before. Fitting the 25 tubes into the boiler space, restricting their movement as expansion and contraction took place with the rise and fall to working temperature and all the while the boiler to be capable of withstanding a maximum pressure of 150psi, as demanded for the Rainhill Trials, required a firm dose of Stephenson perseverance – rewarded by results at Killingworth through their own trial and error approach to its construction. Timothy Young had discounted the stories of Rocket being a breach of Marc Seguin's patent – no-one would steal such a design and then reduce the number of tubes by half, and consequently the heating surface and the capability to generate steam. But if Colborn's assessment was correct, regardless of what calculations Robert Stephenson had made of its potential or adequacy, Rocket needed greater power than demonstrated at Rainhill if it was to regularly haul more than a handful of passengers and a light load of goods the 35 mile journey between Liverpool and Manchester.

Some of the alterations made were superficial and remedied shortcomings shown up at Rainhill, so that for example, the angle of the cylinders was adjusted to smooth out the ride. Others improvements less so. Obtaining increased power would depend on increases to the number of tubes and surface area of the cylinders. Timothy Young had seen reference made to Robert Stephenson increasing the number of tubes virtually fourfold, more than double the number specified in Seguin's patent, and the area of cylinders increased by half again. Even so, after those changes he still apparently needed to increase the boiler length, and thereby the length of each tube, by a further six inches. So too the cylinder bore, from ten to eleven inches, increasing its surface area by a fifth. Robert Stephenson had added progressively more and more tubes to the locomotives he built, with the prospect of delivering more power through the cylinders; power that reached the wheels that drove the locomotive. Those Rocket locomotives, destined to travel between Liverpool and Manchester, had borne little resemblance to the one that competed at Rainhill.

Timothy Young reckoned Robert Stephenson must have thought, with giving more and more surface area for the generation of steam, he was taking no chances, but the way he had increased the surface area seemed haphazard, and seemed never quite enough. And those changes were not the only ones that Timothy Young found had to be made over time to locomotives designed for the Liverpool and Manchester Railway by Robert Stephenson. In fact he was doing little more than firing arrows in the dark, as events after the very Grand Opening of the Liverpool and Manchester Railway on 15th September 1830 showed.

The order for four locomotives was delivered in March 1830. Dart, Comet, Arrow and Meteor were built to the altered specification. Later, to that number were added the North Star and Phoenix, and finally, with most heating tubes of all, the Northumbrian.

Major Pangborn, for Timothy Hackworth Young's benefit, began at the beginning. 'The opening was planned to be a spectacle beyond anything seen at the opening of the Stockton and Darlington Railway. Eight locomotives, dignitaries of the highest order, including the Duke of Wellington, the Iron Duke himself, and several hundred passengers in various carriages. George Stephenson took personal charge of the Northumbrian and it led out the procession of the locomotives. A run between the two centres of industry was to be followed with much celebrations – but a dark cloud was cast over all the best laid plans of mice and men. A fatal accident that befell one of the dignitaries. Rocket ran over William Huskisson, the distinguished MP, whose leg was severed and crushed, injuries from which he did not recover.

Timothy, from what he had meticulously gleaned, had much to add that he felt the Major should consider. 'And the dark cloud remained as far as what Robert Stephenson could accomplish over the running of the locomotives, and the difficulty of making progress on the inclines at Rainhill and Whiston.' He had seen and noted what Henry Booth had written some time after Rainhill, able by then to consider the shortcomings of the locomotives and the contrast with what had been promised and demonstrated.

> "Indeed the feeling at the moment was very prevalent, that it was immaterial whether the Engine travelled up an incline, or on a level...Time and reflection will correct a notion so plausible, but yet so erroneous; otherwise the most grievous disappointments will be the consequence."

Robert had carried out some much needed experiments with Rocket at the end of October, the week after the Rainhill Trials were concluded, as if already heeding Henry Booth's cautions. The results he recorded showed how much the speed up an incline decreased as the weight of loads was increased.

EXPERIMENT FIRST – The "Rocket" Engine, weighing 4 1/4 tons, including the weight of water in the boiler, took a load of

Engine	4 tons	5 cwt
Tender	2 tons	10 cwt
Wagons and Load . .	8 tons	10 cwt

----
15 tons 5 cwt up an inclination of 1 in 96 in 5' 35", the distance being 1 1/2 mile, which is at the rate of 16 miles an hour.

In confirmation of these it may be added, that during several trips
up this plane with a coach containing 30 persons, a speed of 24
miles an hour was maintained.

He reached a speed of 24 mph carrying the weight he had
previously hauled up an incline at Rainhill, passengers
alone in a coach. It was equivalent to 10 tons including
engine, tender and carriage. Increase the load by half and
the speed was reduced by a third. Take twice the load, the
speed reduced to just over half. The three experiments
with proportionate loads of 10, 15 and 20 tons, were,
thought Timothy Young, as though he was trying to
fathom the loss of power imposed through inclines, and
derive some formula or calculation that he could apply,
but that in practice was beyond him.

The first actual runs with the improved 'Rocket-type'
locomotives showed up the shortcomings. Booth's report
nine months after Rainhill was one that Timothy Young
had read particularly carefully.

On the 14th of the present month, (June,)
an experiment was made which may be as a
preliminary measure to a general opening, well
calculated to exhibit the peculiar character of
Railway conveyance, and to put to the test the
capabilities of the Locomotive Engine. On this
occasion the Directors, in two of their carriages
(the one a close glass coach, the other an open

> carriage) proceeded in a journey of inspection from Liverpool to Manchester and back. The Arrow Locomotive, one of the improved Engines on the Rocket principle, was the moving power.

His report was very specific. No single locomotive proved itself powerful enough.

> The gross weight drawn was about 33 tons, consisting as follows:–
> Stone in seven Wagons .... 20 tons.
> Weight of Wagons .... 7 tons
> Engine-tender and 6 persons .... 3 tons
> Two Carriages and 20 persons .... 3 tons
>
> -------
>
> 33 tons
>
> With this load she travelled from the Engine-House, Liverpool, to Oldfield lane Bridge, Salford, Manchester, the distance being about 29 miles, in 2 hours and 25 minutes, including two stoppages to take in water. Up the Whiston inclined plane she was assisted by the Dart, an Engine of similar construction and power, and the first quarter of a mile of the ascent was accomplished at a speed of 17 miles per hour, which, however, decreased to about 4 miles per hour before the summit was gained

Even with locomotives running in pairs, the inclines were actually a formidable obstacle...

Timothy continued. 'He ended up using two locomotives to haul a load of 20 tons of goods. Not what the Directors were expecting. Passenger traffic was all very well but the Bill and the expectations of the promoters of the railway were concerned with improving the handling of goods traffic between the port and the manufacturers.'

'Passengers were being taken right from the start weren't they?' queried the Major. 'Right from the very first week. On the first day 120 passengers and their three tons of luggage. Then more than another 60,000 in less than two months. And all that was required for goods was an assistant locomotive to add its pulling power. Wasn't that just a matter of putting two and two together, doubling the power.'

The locomotive man in Timothy Young came to the fore. 'Doesn't quite work so simply as that.' He showed Major Pangborn the results of Robert Stephenson's Experiments, adding. 'Even when they had been altered, 'Rocket-type' locomotives didn't have the power – weren't up to the job. And the power that was needed to haul goods up any incline far exceeded any calculation that Robert Stephenson had made when he, with his father's approval if not connivance, ran Rocket and a carriage full of passengers up that incline at Rainhill.'

Timothy Young could not believe that ambition had so easily over-ridden the practicalities that were evident to anyone with an engineers mind, accustomed to trying to overcome practical problems. 'And if the Stephensons had only reflected on the successful working of the Stockton and Darlington Railway, which needed a 30HP steam engine at Etherley and a 60HP one at Brusselton, they might have been more prudent and realistic in the claims they made. Perseverance is a great virtue, and had served George Stephenson well, but it doesn't overcome the pull of gravity. Sufficient steam power does that!'

Major Pangborn was nonplussed. He, like much of the world, had the Manchester and Liverpool Railway held up as the paragon of railway development. 'Well if for Rocket, or are we now to call them 'Rocket type' locomotives, it was problematic, how did the other two contenders get on? And what was the answer?'

'Novelty was given a second chance. At Rainhill it had been a firm favourite of the people, and shown the potential of a lighter locomotive. It had every opportunity to make good on the experience of Rainhill.'

Timothy Young had seen the account of the development of Novelty and the outcome. Since it had its supporters on the board, Braithwaite and Ercicsson had been given the opportunity to make good on the defects. They were though required to contract that their locomotive would haul a load of 40 tons gross the 30 miles within 2 hours, consuming less than half a pound of fuel per ton per mile. And match Rocket. And weigh less than 5 tons.

An improved Novelty and two further locomotives were ordered. They were intended to be delivered in time to join in the Grand Opening of the railway, but that was not to be. The locomotives were trialled on the Liverpool and Manchester Railway, which was not without incident when one of the locomotives fell off the line at the high embankment which leads to the Sankey Viaduct. Limited experiments, described in Robert Stephenson's report, came close enough, showing it could carry a load of around 30 tons over the distance. More than a match for a run of Stephenson's 'Arrow' locomotive, but they were eventually withdrawn; built heavier than at Rainhill, raised to an estimated 20 Horse Power, reliant on fans to produce the draught, they were unable to provide sufficient steam for the duration of the journey.

Timothy added the comment that underlined all that his grandfather had succeeded with. 'Steam generation was evidently the issue. As it was for Robert Stephenson. And beating that was down to the blast-pipe.'

Robert Stephenson had banked on multiplying up the power but the extra power he sought in order to create steam was lacking. And for one simple reason. Science hadn't caught up with practice.

Timothy had seen Colborn's report that only after considerable experience on the L&MR had Robert Stephenson and Dewrance carried out experiments; experiments that disappointingly confirmed the multi-tube arrangement was only one third as effective as direct heat. That was their day of reckoning. And for Timothy Young that left them at a disadvantage and several steps behind his grandfather.

In the response to the report from Walker and Rastrick that he had sought to discredit, Robert Stephenson had made the point about practical experience being superior to any scientific or theoretic appraisal. It was well made. Timothy Hackworth, from his days as a blacksmith, knew all about heat travelling along metal that was being worked on. A bar of metal heated in a bed of coals would be safe to handle just a few feet from the red-hot end.

Science, and Robert Stephenson, had no realisation that the heat to raise the steam in the locomotive boiler was all in the first section of the long tubes in a multi-tubular boiler. In those circumstances steam generation was all about the effectiveness of the draught to raise the temperature high enough.

Timothy Young was momentarily back in the roundhouse among the locomotives he kept in service and repair. 'I understand how important that simple device is. And how it has to be set up. Without that know-how Robert Stephenson was always going to struggle.'

Timothy could not avoid being impressed with the efforts that Robert Stephenson made to improve and deliver better performance, but that which seemed plausible was not sufficiently practicable.

'His logic, his calculations, his theories were all wrong and, with what we now know, to no avail. It wasn't until a very erudite French engineer came to Liverpool to conduct experiments that the extent of the power of the blast-pipe came to light – by which time Robert Stephenson was trapped in his pre-occupation with the locomotive chimney as the way to create the draught.'

Major Pangborn had listened to all that Timothy Young had found out. It sounded as though the contenders carried on developing their locomotives, and that it had not been without difficulties. Somehow he thought that the opening and successful running of the Liverpool and Manchester Railway had just followed on from Rainhill. From all that Superintendent Young had to say, evidently not. Major Pangborn took the news to its logical conclusion. Rocket was improved. Novelty was improved. Surely then, Sanspareil must have followed suit. He asked the obvious question. 'How did Sanspareil fare in all this? What did your grandfather do to improve it?'

'Nothing,' Timothy Young replied. 'Well, it was repaired. That was all. The faulty cylinder was replaced. No other change.'

'No change, while Stephenson and Braithwaite and Ercisson virtually redesigned and rebuilt their locomotives? What happened to it?'

A letter, one that Timothy Young had found in the family papers Sam Holmes had sent him, told the story. His grandfather wanted the satisfaction of knowing that Sanspareil had been a worthy contender. Not one just left by the roadside, damaged, disabled by circumstances beyond his control.

'So convinced was Timothy Hackworth of the justness of his cause, he made a bold offer to the directors of the Liverpool and Manchester Railway. He would forfeit the engine if it did not exceed anything performed on the day of the Rainhill Trial; say as a minimum load of 60 tons at 10 miles per hour.'

'That... That is three times more than was called for. And half as much again as was required of Novelty. Was it taken up?'

'Oh yes,' Timothy explained. 'Sanspareil was run again, not on the level but up and down an incline; the same incline that Rocket had taken its load of passengers. Timothy Hackworth ran it, and not just a few times but constantly from mid-morning to six o'clock of the evening. No question as to whether a locomotive designed by him could make the run to Liverpool and back...and there and back again. Then he added a load of 38 tons and ran it up the incline at thirteen-and a-half miles an hour.' Timothy Young had sought out results of other trials to see how that performance compared. They were compelling. He paused before saying, 'The Rocket that Robert Stephenson experimented with only managed to haul 14 tons at that speed. And the much improved 'Arrow' would fall short on the inclines. Now it was no contest again, only this time in favour of Sanspareil.'

'How was that received?' Major Pangborn could only imagine how such a performance from a revitalised Sanspareil would be welcomed?

'Little option really. They agreed to buy it, to honour the offer they made when the competition was first announced.'

'So Sanspareil was one of the locomotives on the line.'

'No. Literally it was sidelined...' Timothy Young had discovered that Ericsson's locomotives had been given the opportunity to trial and run on the track between Liverpool and Manchester. That same courtesy had not been offered to his grandfather. 'Timothy Hackworth had to suffer Sanspareil being relegated to operate on the Bolton and Leigh Railway – a seven mile branch line that joined to the main line.'

Major Pangborn could conjecture the consternation the successful running of Sanspareil caused. 'I'm guessing that neither Stephenson would want to have a locomotive on show that wasn't one of theirs...'

'Or would show up the performance of any of theirs.' Timothy Young barely contained his indignation. 'The superintendent made a report to his directors saying of the performance of Sanspareil on that line 'the like was never done'. On a different line, on a steeper incline than Rainhill, it drew 15 tons over one and a half miles at an average speed of nine miles an hour. And, Sanspareil, unchanged from the locomotive that competed at Rainhill, stayed the distance working continuously without major repair for the next fifteen years. Unlike the locomotives that Robert Stephenson would place on the Liverpool and Manchester Railway.'

Administration building

Golden Door: entrance to the Transportation building

Midway Plaisance

Arabian transport

Crowds on opening day

Transportation building

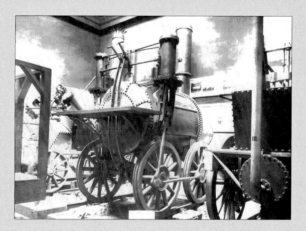
Sanspareil on display

Samson at the Expo

Baltimore & Ohio Railroad Company,
Third Vice President's Office.
Baltimore. June 29, 1892

Mr Samuel Holmes,
100-102 Wall Street, New York.

Dear Sir,

I have your very courteous letter of the 27th instant in answer to mine of June 3rd addressed to the late Mr John Hackworth, Darlington, England.

We are very much pleased indeed to know that at last we are in a position to secure such information as is desired, relative to the inventions & the part played in the development of the locomotive by Timothy Hackworth. There is no question whatever in my mind as regards his being the inventor of the Blast Pipe, & his work generally in connection with the perfection of the locomotive was of the utmost importance: therefore we are most anxious indeed to accord him his deserved place in our exhibit at the World's Colombian Exposition.

Our Mr Pangborn who has designed, & is perfecting, will have sole charge of the exhibit, & will be in New York the latter part of next week, stopping over there from a trip to Northern New York expressly to see you. He will advise before arrival, & will be governed by any hour you may set as most convenient for you to have his company to your house in Elizabeth.

Very truly yours,

(Sgd) C. N. Lord.
Third Vice President

Letter: Charles Lord B&O to Samuel Holmes NRM ref HACK 5/2/2/21

Baltimore & Ohio Railroad letter to Hackworth family

Timothy Hackworth's Invention

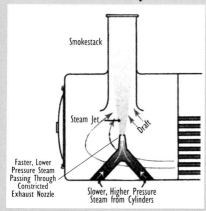

'Blast Pipe'

The invention that gave power to the steam locomotive.

The feature that turned the fortune of the Stockton and Darlington Railway...

And of all who followed after

Without it the locomotive would have run out of steam...

Hackworth's stroke of genius

Simplicity itself – the blast of steam would work just as well as a blast of air

When it was released from a constricted end it would spread out

Just as air did from the bellows in the forge

And fill the chimney ...

And draw behind it a surge of air that would bring a white heat to the coals

The Battle of the Blast Pipe

A pen and ink sketch by S. T. Richardson, published in 1876. It depicts a number of advocates of different inventors fighting for their respective champions. Grasping a massive blast pipe is George Stephenson. The central figure is John Wesley Hackworth dealing blows with his umbrella, impartially on everybody, the reference being to his vigorous advocacy of his father's claim to the invention.

Baltimore, Ma.,
Nov 16th 1892

My dear Aunt,

Your loving letter of Oct 29th (and description of Grandfather's personal appearance) was duly received. I have spent all day today with Major Pangborn, the gentleman who has charge of the B&O exhibit and its presentation. Spent the morning in his office looking over plans and papers, he gave me more information about Timothy Hackworth than I could possibly give him. He had photos and drawings of every Hackworth engine, many of which I never heard of; he also has a large lithograph or engraving with Hackworth's autograph, complete working drawings of "Sans Pareil No1" etc. After luncheon at The Merchants Club we drove out to the workshops. The only completely full size model was that of "Sans Pareil No1" complete in every detail and placed on a few feet of track ready for the Exposition. Possibly you can imagine my feelings as I gazed on this beautiful representation of my Grandfather's genius. A printed card attached to the model will explain the wonders of this engine, the first fitted with the blast pipe as correctly as the most ardent Hackworth admirer could do. In course of conversation he asked if Mr Sam Holmes of New York were my cousin. He said Mr Holmes had invited him to visit him at his country house in Elizabeth N. Y. as he had several plans and papers which would be of interest to him …

Letter: Timothy Hackworth Young to Aunt Prudence NRM ref HACK 4/2/11

Meeting with Major Panghorn – start of the quest

Returning to the description of "Sanspareil", the card continues, "The engine had only commenced running when one of the cylinders cracked through the bore into the steam port extending along its side, the thickness of the metal having been reduced there, by imperfect moulding and boring, to hardly more than a sixteenth of an inch. Its final break-down upon the course was not attributable to any defect in principle of the engine and it was very highly thought of by many of those most competent to judge."

The exhibit was accompanied by a three-quarter size painting of five leading world Locomotive Builders, comprising, George Stephenson, Timothy Hackworth, Horatio Allen, Ross Winans, and Mathew Baldwin. Following up the Baltimore and Ohio R. R. Company's great exhibit at the Chicago Fair, Mr. J. G. Pangborn published the result of his studies on the Locomotive question, and those producing it, in a larger well illustrated volume, named, "The World's Railway," Winchell Printing Co., New York, 1894

In this work he is my decisive; he says referring to the "Royal George": "The four cylinder Engine built by Wilson & Co. for the Stockton and Darlington Road is not a success, and going through a collision has not improved it. Timothy Hackworth, Locomotive Engineer of the Company, determined to rebuild it, and obtained the assent of the Directors to do so only after a good deal of persuasion. The four Stephenson locomotives on the road are not regarded with favour.

THE LOCOMOTIVE AND RAILWAY SYSTEM.

A LETTER FROM THE *London Daily Chronicle*, SEPTEMBER 29TH, 1885.

SIR,—Man's inventive faculty has wonderfully blessed the world in all ages, but of all the products of his genius, or events of his creation, none has so pre-eminently benefited the human race as the locomotive and railway system. Besides being the fruitful parent of innumerable other inventive triumphs, it has practically put the world on wheels, annihilated distance. rendered ponderosity of feather weight, changed the aspects, habits, and customs of society, whose every movement —whether in the pursuit of business, pleasure, or recreation—must be subjected to the inexorable law of railway time.

The railway system affords vast and varied employment to men of every grade and shade of mental and physical capacity. It is the most potent civiliser the ~~genius of man ever devised~~ the most stupendous administrative institution in the world, proof of which we have daily in the innumerable passengers and tons of diversified material hurled to and fro as by magic in this and other countries. In further confirmation, take our magnificent and wondrous postal service, with its ever-extending facilities. Whose imagination could have conceived that a letter costing 1s. 1¼d. 50 years ago is delivered to-day for 1d.? Had Sir Rowland Hill depended upon "horse legs" for establishing his grand penny-post project, it must have remained a mere conception to the end of time! But on the introduction of the "iron steed"—the climax of human ingenuity— even impossibilities became possible. Yet, signal as this triumph is, it simply affords another striking proof of the truth of the proverb, "The world knows little or nothing of its greatest benefactors." It is a fact the parent of this unique device is comparitively unknown! To atone in some degree for this censurable neglect, this article is written by one who 60 years ago was eyewitness to the opening of the first public railway in the world, and having been intimately associated with the developement of the entire system, herein records the facts which constitute the essential history at the time when success or failure was imminent, and when the crowning events which established the system were enacted.

The *first* public railway—both for goods and passengers— was the Stockton and Darlington, opened September 27th, 1825, 20 miles of which were worked by locomotives and horses in competition. The horses proving much more economical during the first 18 months, the directors determined to abandon the locomotives (this would have resulted long before had not Edward Pease and Thomas Richardson, the two railway chieftains, been partners with Stephenson in the Locomotive Works, Newcastle). However, before confirming their decision Timothy Hackworth's opinion was asked, when he proposed to construct an engine capable of working cheaper than *animal power!* After due deliberation, this alternative was adopted "as a *last* locomotive experiment."

The "Royal George" was built at New Shildon by Timothy Hackworth, and tried September, 1827. The first clear years work (1828) she conveyed 22,442 tons of goods over 20 miles at a cost of £466, whereas a corresponding amount of work by horses cost £998, showing a difference in favour of the "Royal George" of £532.

This achievement finally and for ever settled the expediency of the locomotive and railway system. The "steam blast," *Timothy Hackworth's invention*, was first used in this engine.

As George Stephenson has been credited with inventing the "steam blast," a quotation from a letter written by his own hand to Timothy Hackworth, settles the point. The letter (which is now in the writer's possession) is dated Liverpool, July 25, 1828 : "We have tried the new engine ('Lancashire Witch') at Bolton ; we have also tried the blast to it, and I believe it will answer. There are two bellows worked by excentrics underneath the tender." The bellows did not answer, and it is obvious that at this date Stephenson knew nothing of the steam blast.

Smiles says, in "Life of George Stephenson," page 167 : "The true founder of the railway system was the man who invented such a locomotive as made railway locomotion practicable and profitable." We accept Smiles's version, and submit that the foregoing and following facts conclusively prove to whom the merit belongs.

Before the advent of the "Royal George" the Stockton and Darlington shares, originally £100 each, had declined below £50 each. Six years later (1833) their value was £300 each. In 1833 Timothy Hackworth contracted for working the Stockton and Darlington Railway. He took the works, the locomotives, and all thereto belonging at a valuation, paying the company five per cent. interest thereon, found all material and workmen for repairing and working the engines for four-tenths of a penny per ton (of goods) per mile, exclusive of carriages laden and empty ; whereas as late as 1834 —when Hackworth's contract was going on—it cost the Liverpool and Manchester railway (George and Robert), 1⅛d. per gross ton per mile—i.e., weight of carriages included, which, constituting about half the weight, raises the *about* cost to 3⅜d. per ton per mile. This, compared with Hackworth's contract price of four tenths of one penny, shows a marvellous contrast. It was through the counsel of Timothy Hackworth and practical data from his "Royal George" that the directors of the Liverpool and Manchester Railway abandoned the stationary engine and rope system recommended by their deputation—Messrs. Rasterick and Walker. These facts incontrovertibly prove the author of the locomotive and railway system to have been Timothy Hackworth, who was born December 22, 1786, at Wylam-on-Tyne, where he introduced the locomotive in 1811, the merit of which has been erroniously ascribed to William Hedley, the viewer.   WYLAM.

John Wesley Hackworth – Fighting his father's cause

CHAPTER SIXTEEN

Deliver the goods

Exposition site, Same day

Major Pangborn could see that Timothy Young had the bit firmly between his teeth. It was no more than he had asked of him but this was turning up more material than he could have imagined. Or, given his reporters instinct, more than was needed to tell a simple enough story to be taken on board by the public at large. 'Timothy, of course you have to follow up the work of your grandfather. Remember there is only so much material we need for the display by the portraits in the Inventors Gallery.'

Timothy Young had come to the realisation just how much had rested on the outcome of the Rainhill Trials. It had been a calamity for his grandfather as the Major had suggested. Surely though his grandfather's skill and inventiveness, even if it had been sidelined, would not have been diminished by this one setback. There would be more that he had accomplished in designing locomotives. More than the combined practical accomplishments of the Stephensons. More to tell.

In the face of all that Timothy Young had uncovered, Major Pangborn needed to clear his head. With a cheery,

'We ought to meet up tomorrow morning, Timothy. Time to settle on those displays now that the carpenters have the building of them underway,' he set his face towards the open space of the exposition grounds and the Midway Plaisance. The look he saw on Timothy Young's face had turned from indignation to mild consternation, so he added 'Any time you feel as though you need to lift your spirits, take the time for a gentle stroll down the Midway. We have made our mark there too. Paris had a tower built by Mr Eiffel. A wonderful structure. A wonder to behold. Before that your country had a stupendous glass building for its Great Exhibition in 1851 – acres of glass, the size of a palace, a crystal palace. We have a magnificent piece of American engineering, a giant metal structure taller than the Eiffel tower. A huge wheel that revolves and transports visitors over two hundred and fifty feet up into the skies, way above all the buildings.'

Timothy Young turned his head towards the Major, who had stopped to take the moment he needed to lighten the day for his assistant.

'There's a transport of delight, Timothy. Two thousand people at a time, sitting and standing in hanging carriages as they see below them the enormity of what America can put on show'. He chuckled as he imagined the headline in the Chicago Tribune: FERRIS POWERS PAST EIFFEL. 'A trip in the wheel built by George Washington Ferris is all the lift you ever need while you are working here, Timothy.'

As he left, Timothy had returned to going through the boxes of family correspondence and records that his cousin, Sam Holmes, had sent through. Perhaps, Major Pangborn thought, he had encouraged him too much.

The turn-round in the affairs of the Stockton and Darlington Railway after the success of Royal George provided the bedrock on which Timothy Hackworth would come into his own. A revision to the original Parliamentary Bill would bring about far reaching changes; a railway line extending to a new deepwater port. The inclusion in the preamble to the very first bill of the haulage of iron ore and limestone, in addition to coal, foresaw the potential of the untapped mineral wealth of the region. All the figures underestimated the extent to which the railway would underpin its exploitation and change the face of the North East of England.

The year before Rainhill, when the directors of the Liverpool and Manchester Railway were still debating the pros and cons of whether they would even proceed with the locomotive, those involved with the Stockton and Darlington Railway had taken a decisive move. Several hundred acres of land were purchased to house the industry, trade and workers that would result – and the ingenuity of their railway superintendent would be called on the following year to make the expansion a practical proposition. Over time a whole new town, Middlesbrough, would be created. A second town to add to the already burgeoning Shildon. One that would also owe its existence to the arrival of the Stockton and Darlington Railway.

In 1829 the number of coal mines had been increased and consequently the amount of coal that had to be handled. Moving the loading arrangements downriver would enable larger vessels to be serviced, and the new port would require more efficient ways to handle the increased traffic.

Months before the Rainhill trial was advertised, the directors of the Stockton and Darlington Railway launched their own competition for the design of an improved set of 'staithes', or arrangements of loading points to deliver the goods from the wagons into the holds of ships. Before his trial at Rainhill Timothy Hackworth had won that competition, and the £157 10s premium, with a bold and ingenious engineering solution. His steam powered staithes would allow the simultaneous operation of six loading bays. Just as he had with increasing the effectiveness of winding arrangements at the powerful stationery engines in the line, he used the counterweight of the wagon to be loaded next as it descended to draw up the wagon that had just released its load into the ship's hold. His design called for less steam power than would otherwise have been required. 'Economy and efficiency' were his watchwords as ever.

The increasing success of the railway also required a new locomotive and Timothy Hackworth completed the design a few months after his return from Rainhill. Early the following year he had gained the approval of the board for a new 'swift' engine. As always it was to be built by Robert Stephenson & Co

Timothy Young had uncovered a letter from his Uncle John that gave details of the development of the new locomotive:

"In one of my father's memorandum books I find he started on a journey Monday morning 7 o'clock March 1st, 1830, from Shildon to Stockton, Stranton, Sunderland, North and South Shields, Newastle and Bedlington. He

arrived at Newcastle, Wenesday 3rd, took a gig and in company with a Mr Dickinson (an official of R. Stephenson & Co.), went to Bedlington to order the boiler plates for the "Globe", they returned to Newcastle and Father spent great part of Thursday 4th, Friday 5th and Saturday 6th at Forth Street Works giving designs, instructions and seeking out patterns for the "Globe". She is called in some places "Small locomotive new construction" and in others the "Swift engine", but I ascertained from dear Father that both these terms referred to the "Globe" engine. In a subsequent entry I find that R. Stephenson & Co. received the boiler plates from Bedlington for the "Swift engine," April 4th, 1830."

The introduction to the letter was a surprise to him, with the reference to what else had happened.

"I had an idea that something was going on with regard to the "Crank shaft, etc." as your application is not the first I have had on the subject....the fact that no sooner had Messrs. Stephenson & Co. secured the order for the "Globe" then they commenced and finished an engine with a "Crank shaft" (called by the name of some Planet or Star, no doubt of the first magnitude), I believe for the L. & M. Railway Co. previous to sending the "Globe" here.

Timothy Young discovered that a new locomotive was supplied to the Liverpool and Manchester Railway in the October of 1830, while the 'Globe' was not delivered till two months later. Elements of the design had been adopted for this new locomotive, named 'Planet', not withstanding that an official at Robert Stephenson & Co had originally objected to the design of the cranked axle on the grounds that 'it would involve a loss of power, as the efficient length of lever could only be calculated from the inside of the journal to the axle's centre.'

The Globe reached the Stockton and Darlington Railway in December 1830, delayed by nine months in the works of Robert Stephenson & Co, and on the 27th of that month the engine made its first regular journey, the occasion being the opening of the new line from Darlington to Middlesbrough. After this it worked the passenger train with great success for nearly nine years. It was said to have attained high speed and a steadiness hitherto unknown, and to have run at the rate of 50 miles per hour.

There was much that was enhancing the operation of the Stockton and Darlington Railway under the management by his grandfather.

Robert Stephenson too had to provide a new locomotive. Approval of the Liverpool and Manchester Railway was based on the claim in the Parliamentary Bill that goods would be carried by locomotive at the rate of 10s per ton, compared to the 15s per ton merchants were previously charged for using the canals. The locomotive Planet was developed to meet that need. In this case to demonstrate the running of a goods service as originally intended, capable of being developed to transport up to 2000 tons of goods a day.

So far he had delivered several Rocket-type locomotives – Meteor, Comet, Dart and Arrow then Phoenix and North Star, finally the Northumbrian. A way of working them up the inclines on the line was established and was proving adequate for the carriage of passengers. It was also producing much welcomed revenue at rates far in excess of those that would be applicable to goods traffic; passengers paying the equivalent of 60s per ton for their journeys.

Timothy Young had noted the continuing alterations to the original Rocket design as he uncovered the details of the locomotives supplied for the Liverpool and Manchester Railway. More tubes, then longer tubes, would add more than power. They would also add weight. The original requirement, so as to reduce the weight borne by the rails and the load on the wheels, was for a locomotive of less than six tons and preferably below four-and-a-half tons. 'Arrow', he discovered, weighed in at six tons. The 'Northumbrian', with its number of tubes increased to 150, came through heavier still. They had both been put through their paces well before the official opening in September.

Arrow in June 1830 had been taken out to put on a show for the directors, taking them from Liverpool to Manchester in two carriages – one of which was enclosed by glass – and hauling a twenty-ton load at just above the Rainhill requirement of 10 miles per hour. When it climbed an incline, even assisted by a sister locomotive, Dart, the speed fell to 4 miles per hour. On the return journey with only carriages and passengers as the load, Arrow powered up the incline on its own, much as Rocket had done at Rainhill.

The Northumbrian had been further modified and was described as having part of the exhaust steam being taken as a draught beneath the fire grate to enliven the heat source. Just as Uncle John had described of Royal George three years earlier. Riding on the Northumbrian on the 11th September an engineer called Naysmith reported that, with George Stephenson as driver and Robert as stoker, it had achieved 30 mph on several short trips without load.

There was, though, pressure from merchants and the directors to open the line to transport of goods to reap the benefits of the economies of the locomotive and avoid the excessive costs and delays incurred by canal. More powerful locomotives were needed in order to draw the much greater weights involved, and overcome the inclines. Stephenson and Co were not the only locomotive manufacturers that the Liverpool and Manchester Railway was considering. Edward Bury & Co had a locomotive of their design already trialled on the line. Timothy Young thought there would have been an urgency about introducing Planet, proving the design and providing delivery in time to counter any threat to the dominance of the Stephensons.

Planet was not put through its paces until December, some six weeks after it had been delivered to the Liverpool and Manchester Railway. This heavier, more powerful locomotive, designed for use with the goods traffic, took a sample load in eighteen wagons: 135 bags of American cotton, 200 barrels of flour, 63 sacks of oatmeal, and 34 sacks of malt. Altogether a weight of 50 tons, to which had to be added 30 tons for the wagons, the tender and water and 15 passengers. The report described the ascent up the incline as being assisted 'by other engines' at a speed of nine miles an hour, similar to the speed overall. Afterwards, Henry Booth had written;

'Taking this performance as a fair criterion, which there is no reason to doubt, for engines of the same class as the Planet (with the assistance of one large Engine, constructed for the purpose, up the inclined plane,) would be capable of taking upon the Railway, all the cotton which passes between Liverpool and Manchester.'

Clearly with the suggestion of the need for 'one large engine', as yet to be built, it was not all that Robert Stephenson had hoped for.

Timothy Young found Robert Stephenson would later, when other railway schemes were proposed, come to accept the punishing nature of inclines and their adverse effect on locomotive power. It was reported he had also, in Planet, brought into use the constricted blast-pipe in conjunction with, and while also still favouring, the tall chimney as a source of air flow to increase the heat source.

Robert Stephenson's early encounter with the draught produced through a chimney had years before resulted in a locomotive with a 16-feet high chimney, which could be extended a further 8 feet. Rocket was noted for having a tall chimney – up to the height limit set for Rainhill – and of it giving a swaying motion to the locomotive. Rastrick, one of the Rainhill judges, had already raised the chimney to 14-feet on his Agenoria locomotive for the Shutt End Railway. And on an Arrow-type locomotive that was delivered to Leicester & Swannington the chimney was sufficiently at the limit that it was felled by the first tunnel it encountered.

However Timothy Young looked at it, Robert Stephenson was fumbling his way in pursuit of the power he was lacking in the locomotive and so desperately needed to find for the Liverpool and Manchester Railway. His grandfather was experiencing no such difficulties. The blast-pipe was the salvation.

Timothy had found the work of the French engineer, Francois de Pambour, among the technical papers that Major Pangborn had provided. His was a first explanation of the effect of the blast-pipe, but it was not discovered until 1836. Experimental work on the Liverpool and Manchester Railway, several years after the opening, showed that the blast-pipe gave a vaporisation of water more than five times that of the locomotive at rest. The evaporative force of a locomotive was multiplied several times over given the correct use of such a simple device – a device that was entirely due to his grandfather. He had also discovered that the extent to which a single, centred orifice was constricted affected its efficiency. Too much and the front section of the tubes would be subject to extreme heat. Too little and the impact would be insufficient to adequately heat the tubes.

Evaporative force, Timothy Young was aware, was in practice the defining feature of the power of the steam locomotive, not its weight or the consumption of fuel which appeared to have pre-occupied early locomotive engineers. You had to get that right.

It would affect Robert Stephenson's efforts and underpin Timothy Hackworth's locomotive design. Robert Stephenson had a blast-pipe sited at the base of the chimney in Planet, and also retained a tall chimney. The former would be of little effect, the latter would be all that was doing the work to produce an airflow. Timothy Hackworth understood what he was doing. He had with Royal George brought into play a single, centrally placed and constricted orifice. It would create a vortex – an inverted cone of steam that filled the chimney and, reaching high enough, would create a vacuum and draw a strong draught to urge the fire. His grandson had seen for himself the record of the effect that had on the performance of the locomotives on the Stockton and Darlington Railway. There was good cause to celebrate the advent of Royal George.

Timothy Young imagined there would be a price the Liverpool and Manchester Railway would have to pay for Robert Stephenson's lack of practical experience, and for the complexity of the science needed to formulate dependable rules for the design of locomotives. He would also be surprised if the Stockton and Darlington Railway did not continue to reap a financial reward from the sagacity of its Locomotive Superintendent, Timothy Hackworth.

CHAPTER SEVENTEEN

Where will it end?

Exposition site, Same day

Major Pangborn had taken the Intramural railway to the Midway. His interest had been piqued by one particular sight at the Arabian Village and, along with a handful of early fairgoers taking advantage of cheap entrance tickets in the weeks before the official opening, he spent the afternoon discovering more about it.

The exhibit put on display all manner of aspects of Arabian life. Especially expected to draw the crowds were the men riding on horseback with their spears, and the warriors with their unusual dress, their long ornate rifles and flourishing their fearsome-looking scimitars. He though was considerably more interested in the demonstration of the way they made use of camels.

The part of the exhibit that had caught his eye was an arrangement for travel he had never seen before. A camel was being exercised in the arena where the displays of horsemanship would be put on show. Pangborn watched intently as it was being led around by a man in native dress. In the stead of any normal saddle arrangement, the camel had what looked like two individual conical tents, perched, one across each side of the animal. From what he could make out, each tent structure was there to provide shade above a panier, and the panier was big enough to house a single passenger, whose head he could see poking out through the flaps of the canopy. The Arabs had contrived a way to double up on the transport capacity of a camel. Never before had he imagined there could be any such way of transport, and he prided himself that he had seen all manner of variations in his pursuit of steam passenger transport.

One thought would not leave him. The thought that he had seen, set up here at the Exposition, other equally distinctive and quite different forms of transport from across the world. The Esquimaux tribes that had set up camp had used dog sleds on land and paddled across water in kayaks. The Laplanders had brought their reindeer. He had heard of large sleds being used across snow-covered land in Russia. All of which added another dimension to his theme and the very idea of 'Transportation'. A theme that he thought with all the exhibits that had been assembled could, and maybe should, live on beyond the life of the Exposition.

He walked past part of the Midway on his way to visit the exhibitors in the State Building of California before making his return journey to the Administration Offices, looking with fresh eyes at the displays of the various nations. He passed the Lapland Village, then the Tunisian encampment sited below the shadow of the giant Ferris Wheel. That was followed by the Turkish Village with a commanding main square and, sited opposite, the German Village, until in turn he passed the Javanese Village that was further along still. All very exotic and different to anything that the average Americans would have encountered in their lives.

The garish and extravagant posters, if not the sounds of elephants trumpeting and the muted roar of lions, told him he was passing by the site of Hagenbach's Animal Show and nearing the turning point that would set him down the walkway towards the Esquimaux tribe encampment beside the small North West Lake. The possibilities as to what he might accomplish when this exposition came to its ending stirred his imagination.

Timothy Young was relying far less on his imagination and considerably more on the facts of railway life. Head down, he was taking in all that reportedly happened as the Liverpool and Manchester Railway moved forward. Robert Stephenson came across difficulties that took time to surmount.

The multi-tubular boilers were not the easy solution to the problems of having sufficient power. They became prone to the copper tubes becoming clogged with fuel residue and, much as it had been difficult to get the tubes set in the boiler in the first place, cleaning, clearing and replacing them was a major repair job. So too was the failure of the wheels, which was alleviated by the introduction of wooden spokes with their flexibility that made them less prone to breakage – and a reduction in the weight to be carried on the rails. He had found numerous debates and exchanges in Mechanics Magazine about locomotive failures and concerns about repairs. Reliability and economy of purpose were the rallying cries.

Also up for debate was the topic of the failure to offer the goods service that had been committed to when the railway was first authorised. Passengers were an inviting and lucrative market; an unexpected bonus that kept the enterprise financially afloat. However, the observations by Henry Booth, Secretary to the Liverpool and Manchester Railway, had to be heeded. There was a need for still more powerful engines to replace the multiple assistant engines in use simply to overcome the inclines with the heavy traffic of goods. More power would mean more weight; the pursuit of which was not a virtuous circle of improvements.

Zerah Colborn was quite pointed, even to the extent of describing a detailed schedule of failings of the locomotives on the Liverpool and Manchester Railway. Not holding back from stating the concerns of an engineer, he was equally forthright in his view of the costs of repairs which, "applied to engines but two or three years from the maker's workshops, proclaim such defects of original structure as to make it almost a matter of wonder that the Liverpool and Manchester line was worked at all." And he cited the observations of Pambour in the experiments held there.

Pambour in his studies of the railway reported what he saw. Timothy Young was taken aback when he read of the extent of the difficulties. In 1834 Pambour had noted:

"it is necessary to mention what is meant by repairs to the engines, is nothing less than their complete re-construction; that is to say that when an engine requires any repair, unless it is for some trifling accident, it is taken to pieces and a new one constructed, which receives the same name as the first, and in the construction of which are made to serve all such parts of the old engine as

> are still capable of being used with advantage. The consequence of this is that a re-constructed or repaired engine is literally a new one. The repairs amount thus to considerable sums, but they include also the renewal of the engines."

Pambour also had discovered that, over the time since the opening, the locomotives provided for the Liverpool and Manchester Railway had not stood up to the rigours of the work. He had observed and commented:

> "We have said elsewhere that the Liverpool and Manchester Railway Company possesses at present thirty locomotive engines. It must not be concluded, however, that that number is necessary in order to execute the above said haulage. Of these 30 engines about one third are useless. They are the most ancient which, having been constructed at the first establishment of the railway, at a time when the company had not yet obtained sufficient experience in that respect, are found now to be out of proportion with the work required of them.
>
> The engines actually in daily activity on the road amount to about 10 or 11, with an equal number in repair or reserve the business might completely be ensured. This is in fact what happens at present, the surplus above that number, being nearly abandoned."

Timothy Young looked long and hard at the performance figures Pambour had collected. The number of locomotives in operation fell well short of the number that was supposed to be required to haul the quantity of goods. And the amount of goods being carried was barely a quarter of the original scheme. He wondered whether the anticipated powerful locomotives that Henry Booth had advocated had ever appeared.

Among the many articles in the Mechanics Magazine that openly questioned the operation of the Liverpool and Manchester Railway was one that described what changes had been put into effect. The locomotives in use had become one of three designated types: train, luggage and bank-engines. Train engines were 30 horsepower and weighed 8 tons. Luggage engines were 35 horsepower and weighed 9 tons. Bank-engines were 50 horsepower, weighed 12 tons and were used for assisting trains up the inclined planes on the line. So, thought Timothy, Henry Booth prevailed; the locomotives were named 'Samson' and 'Goliath', so all would have been aware that the names they bore reflected their considerable power. But it put them some long way from the six-ton limit originally planned for the weight of locomotive that would serve the needs of the railway. Undoubtedly as continually heavier locomotives were introduced to the Liverpool and Manchester Railway they would have strained the original rail track to breaking point, and it would have needed replacing. He turned to other reports to discover how the heavier, stronger locomotives had fared.

Evidently Stephenson's 'Planet-type' locomotives had proved not powerful enough. The directors apparently found the method of working their heavy trains with four or five locomotives was far from economical for the goods traffic. Hence the bank-engines. Originally on four wheels, 'Samson' was delivered in January, 1831 and came into operation a month later. It hauled a train of goods and wagons of more than 150 tons from Liverpool to Manchester in two-and-a-half hours. It lacked stability though and, as Timothy Hackworth had accomplished with the design of Royal George years before, shortly after its introduction the Stephensons changed it to a six-wheeled locomotive.

So, the Stephenson's had come to a conclusion that Timothy Hackworth knew instinctively; there were as they say 'horses for courses'. The ways by which passenger and goods traffic had to be handled were as different as the nature of them, as were the locomotives to do that. And, as he had written to Robert Stephenson, a 'swift' train on a double track "may be used to the utmost advantage – improvements, upon anything yet produced of greater importance, in all respects, are clearly practicable."

Royal George had the power, and met the demands on the Stockton and Darlington for goods haulage. The Globe, much lighter, produced sufficient power and efficiency of running for passenger transport. The track on the Stockton and Darlington was laid as double the year after the fanfare of the grand opening of Liverpool and Manchester Railway, in anticipation of and in readiness for expanding traffic being carried on their railway. His grandfather would then also have introduced further improvements in the design of his locomotives.

Timothy Young found what he was looking for in the correspondence that his cousin Sam Holmes had included in the bundles he sent through. Dated 8th November 1831 was a letter from R Stephenson and Co to his grandfather, concerning a new design of a locomotive of improved performance. It made the third occasion when they had intervened in his business – first the poor casting of the cylinders for his locomotive Sanspareil, then the contention that his offset crank was not workable followed by the delays in fabricating and delivery of Globe. Now they were declining to make this latest locomotive to his grandfather's design because it violated a patent. They, also, had written to Mr Pease, as director of the Stockton and Darlington Railway, bringing it to his attention and asking his advice.

Timothy found the details of the locomotive in question in 'Practical Mechanics Journal'. His grandfather had evidently thought about the multi-tubular boiler, or more especially the problem it faced with the reduction of heat conducted along the length of the tubes. And thereby the capability to produce a strong continuous supply of steam – the lifeblood of the locomotive. Timothy Young found in Colborn's book descriptions of relevant heating experiments carried out in 1858, but they were not conducted in sufficient time to have any impact on the designs of Robert Stephenson and Company in the 1830s for the locomotives of the Liverpool and Manchester Railway. They did though show that the heat from the first foot of tube diminished by 20 per cent in the second foot, and by the same amount again in the third, finally by a further 10 per cent in the fourth foot, reducing it to around half overall. Science, more than fifteen years later, had again eventually caught up with his grandfather's practical experience, inventiveness and engineering know-how.

Applying his blacksmith's knowledge, Timothy Hackworth would have related it to being able to handle metal bars within a few feet of the end that was white hot in the heat of the furnace. His inventive solution, to take maximum advantage of the increased surface area offered by the use of tubes, had been to limit the tube length to four feet and to insert them into the backplate of the flue, thus combining them with the powerful heat source of his return flue in the boiler. A hybrid solution that offered the best of both worlds – a multi-tube return flue boiler that offered increased power, reliability and ease of maintenance.

His grandfather had conceived, designed and specified such an arrangement before any patent was lodged. However, so far as the Stephensons were concerned, the person claiming the patent was a man of considerable standing; Napier, the eminent marine engineer.

Timothy recognised the handwriting of Uncle John below the contents of the troublesome letter sent by Robert Stephenson and Company.

His grandfather had, with good cause and in good faith, swiftly dealt with the matter. It also confirmed how little was known or understood by the Stephensons of his work, but spoke volumes of their keeping abreast of and avoiding patented work.

"Hackworth immediately got in communication with Robert Napier who had just patented the return multi-tubular firetube, which came to be so extensively used in marine engines. Napier then came to Shildon, being speedily satisfied that the invention had been used by Hackworth before the patent had been taken out. It was agreed that each should take his own course with regard to the future use and that neither would interfere with the

other. This matter being amicably settled Napier remained for some days as Hackworth's guest and the two parted with mutual expressions of esteem. Shortly after his departure the family received from Napier a Scotch Mull as a little memento of his pleasant visit."

In contrast to the intervention, Napier and Hackworth had met convivially and resolved things professionally and as equals. And Hackworth was confirmed as the moving and inventive force of another step forward. The return multi-tube boiler resolved the shortcoming of the delivering heat through multiple tubes, and was so arranged that the practical problems of the repair of such tubes that was required in use could be accomplished without the taking apart and rebuilding of the locomotive.

And Timothy had seen that Colborn had identified such repair costs as a considerable expenditure for the Liverpool and Manchester Railway up to 1833, by which time the copper tubes in the locomotives were replaced by brass tubes, being heavier but more durable, and importantly resistant to 'burn out'.

The recent letter from Cousin Sam was crystal clear as to the direction his grandfather had taken. While the Stephensons were engaging themselves in the construction of the railways that were spreading throughout England, he was attending to the running of the line and constructing locomotives. Timothy read through the first page again, which was Sam's response to his comments about the development of locomotives for the Stockton and Darlington Railway.

213

NEW YORK AND PACIFIC STEAMSHIP, COAL
AND LUMBER COMPANY.

DIRECT STEAMSHIP LINE
BETWEEN
NEW YORK AND PACIFIC COAST.
MONTHLY SAILINGS.

MORRIS BUILDING,
64, 66 & 68 BROAD STREET.

SAMUEL HOLMES, General Agent.
Cable Address: Holmes, New York.
Watkins & Scott's 10th Edition Codes.
Telephone Call: 1010 Broad.

NEW YORK, 18 April 1893

Dear Cousin Tim,

You are right. Grandfather never stopped his work
with locomotives even though he was less than pleased
with the outcome at Rainhill. He was though satisfied that
when Sanspareil was repaired and placed on the line that
it performed as he had calculated and expected. His future
would still be with locomotives, and with the Stockton and
Darlington Railway.

He had already designed the staithes at Middlesborough
for loading. He had introduced a 'swift' train, in the form
of the 'Globe', that was suitable for passenger traffic.
The goods traffic was increasing and more powerful
locomotives were called for. So he had turned his ingenuity
and experience to good purpose. He designed two types of
improved locomotives, 'Majestic' and 'Wilberforce' classes,
six wheeled locomotives, based round two arrangements
for the boiler. 'Majestics' had a 13 foot boiler, combining a
single flue with more than a hundred tubes, just four foot
long. The later 'Wilberforces' were more compact with an
8 foot boiler, surrounded by tubes along its the length,
incorporating a return flue. They were the equal of the
Stephenson designed heavy locomotives from when their
'Planet' and 'Rocket' style locomotives were faltering with
the carriage of goods on their railways.

NEW YORK AND PACIFIC STEAMSHIP, COAL AND LUMBER COMPANY
MORRIS BUILDING, 64, 66 & 68 BROAD STREET NEW YORK
Cable Address: Holmes, New York

Continuing to work on the Stockton and Darlington Railway line up to 1846, those same locomotives had the endorsement 'take them, weight for weight, they surpass any engine on the line.' Tribute enough, if any were needed, to the skill of the work and long standing benefit given the railway by grandfather.

Sam's letter continued, setting out the way in which Timothy Hackworth had followed his own path through the further development of the locomotive, sustaining the commerce and the financial rewards of the railway.

A most agreeable part of events in the life of our grandfather was his extreme attachment to Mr Joseph Pease, the first Quaker Member of Parliament; a gentleman of very great culture. It was a great pleasure to hear him speak, for as well as having a musical voice he had much to say that was worthwhile.

He realized the spiritual view Mr Pease took as a Quaker, and his own practical engineering mind realized too, that unless religion had its seat within you, it was of very little account. His Methodist belief adhered to the plain practical fact, the "Kingdom of God is within you."

He knew and Mr Pease knew, and revelled in the accompanying fact, that spiritual life was the result of the fruits of the Spirit; "Love. Joy, peace, long suffering, gentleness, goodness, faith, meekness, temperance; being cultivated and exhibited to the world." It was a bond between the Director of the railway and his locomotive engineer.

NEW YORK AND PACIFIC STEAMSHIP, COAL AND LUMBER COMPANY
MORRIS BUILDING, 64, 66 & 68 BROAD STREET NEW YORK
Cable Address: Holmes, New York

Out of the strength of that came the arrangement, settled between them in 1833, for grandfather to contract to run the railway for the Stockton and Darlington Railway Company. He would take over the locomotives, the men and pay interest on the capital. He would also set up his own workshops for the repair and construction of locomotives for the railway. It was Mr Joseph Pease who gave the name "Soho" to Timothy Hackworth's works.

Grandfather set a standard that few could match. He agreed to haul goods at the cost of four tenths of a penny per ton per mile. An arrangement that held good for seven years until 1840; throughout a time when trade and traffic was expanding all the while.

NEW YORK AND PACIFIC STEAMSHIP, COAL AND LUMBER COMPANY
MORRIS BUILDING, 64, 66 & 68 BROAD STREET NEW YORK
Cable Address: Holmes, New York

His grandfather, Timothy Hackworth, had taken the boldest of steps. At a time when estimates of costs to do with the railway were notoriously exceeded in practice, he fixed the contract price at which he would run the railway. Like his other observations, the pricing of such an arrangement must have been determined by his skill and informed by years of accumulated know-how and experience that had already proved beneficial to the Stockton and Darlington Railway. It would certainly only be made, particularly at the level he set, were he confident that ongoing costs, specifically for the repair of the locomotives he took responsibility for, were contained. It would only be successful if he was right.

One thing any locomotive man was sure of was that keeping the locomotives going is as important a part of a railway as building them in the first place. Timothy Young, as a foreman of the Chicago, Milwaukee, St Paul Railroad, had experienced at first hand the impact on repair costs of engineering quality, and the considerable part it plays in keeping the railway operating and in good shape. Efficiency and economy were part of the creed of Quakers and Methodists alike, indeed they were their watchwords.

He put the letter to one side

Major Pangborn breezed in, on his timetable he and Timothy Young had a week to finalise the information for display alongside the portraits in the Inventors Gallery. The notable American pioneers had been a straightforward proposition. He had accumulated more than enough material, and deciding on the layout of the various display panels was just that, a matter of layout. It took him back to his newspaper reporter days of establishing the story, picking out a catching headline and mixing some pictures with the text. He had a head-start on Timothy: George Stephenson, Rocket, the Manchester and Liverpool Railway were the striking contribution of that pioneer. He also, with Timothy's help, would have enough background about Royal George and the first railway for public use – the Stockton and Darlington Railway.

Timothy Young knew that Major Pangborn wanted to settle the details of the displays for his grandfather and his contribution. There would be no problem in telling the story of the blast-pipe. The facts of what it achieved spoke for themselves. So too did the struggles of Robert Stephenson to develop his locomotives, a veritable battle when compared to the ease with which his grandfather had delivered powerful locomotives. He still had the last of the contributions from Aunt Pru to investigate, but apart from that he had followed a clear path of his grandfather's contribution to the development of the locomotive. The expansion of the Stockton and Darlington Railway stood side by side with that of the Liverpool and Manchester Railway. Time to speak out. It was what he had been sent to do.

'Major?'

'We have work to do, Timothy. The display... I thought a focus on the Stockton and Darlington Railway. And then, from what you have found, the prowess of Royal George and the invention of the 'blast-pipe'.'

'I have found so much more about what you would call the prowess of my grandfather. In so many ways he made the locomotive a workable proposition where others did not or even could not.'

'Timothy there's a limit to what we need to put in front of the public for them to get that sense of what it must have been like in the early times, when locomotive transport was accomplished by the pioneers.'

Timothy looked at the stack of books and journals that had become his library. He took stock. He had explored the life of his grandfather through the innovations he had brought into use. More than just a single locomotive, altogether more than any other locomotive engineer had accomplished. And the railway he worked for was the first in the world, even if that was little known outside the North East of England. He had no intention of playing lip-service to the accomplishments of his grandfather.

'Major, let me go through those events in my grandfather's work, which was the foundation of the railway at Shildon. The locomotives he devised were the backbone of the Stockton and Darlington Railway. His innovation and engineering skill kept them in the front of the locomotive revolution. Ahead of the Stephensons, who fumbled in their support of the Liverpool and Manchester Railway. Who struggled to deliver what they had promised. My grandfather was a man who never contemplated or promised anything of his locomotives that he could not deliver. His know-how was exceptional... as was his inventive mind and he put his money where his mouth was. Not once, when he paid for his locomotive Sanspareil out of his own pocket. But again when he committed to run a railway at a price that others could not contemplate. He made sure the railway he worked for stayed as the first among equals...'

CHAPTER EIGHTEEN

A time of reckoning

Baltimore, Tuesday 11th April 1893

The familiar building on the corner of Baltimore Street and Calvert that Major Joseph Pangborn approached was never intended to be ignored or overlooked. Five storeys of granite and brickwork continually reflected the substance of the Baltimore and Ohio Railroad itself. It stood out from the crowd. Momentarily he paused, looking up at the colonnaded battlements of the railway company's head office.

Vice President Charles Lord had asked him to visit, wanting to hear what could now be contributed to honour the inventiveness of locomotive pioneer, Timothy Hackworth, the engine builder of Shildon. He wondered how much the grandson had found out about his grandfather and the locomotives of the Stockton and Darlington Railway. Wondered whether this man had been able, with their help, to do what the Hackworth family over the years had found themselves unable.

The elevator stopped on the fourth floor and Major Pangborn walked a familiar route down the corridor, past the boardroom, stopping in front of the second office door beyond. He gave a polite knock and without further ado opened the door and walked in. Charles Lord looked up, signalled for him to take the chair to the left of his desk. The Major waited while the paperwork on Charles Lord's desk was completed, folded neatly up and placed securely out of sight in one of the drawers that graced the impressive desk.

'Well, Joseph. Here we are, three weeks to the grand opening. All well I trust?'

'It truly is a splendid site, Charles. The world will see what our young country has accomplished. So much that is new. So much to experience and enjoy.'

'How have you and young Mr Hackworth got on? Have the gaps you had in locomotive history now been filled? Has it all been as we had hoped?'

Joseph Pangborn was happy to give an affirmative answer. 'Most definitely. Mr Timothy has turned up information in the family correspondence from Hackworth's son about the early running of Royal George, and from the records of the drivers. And the effect of the extra power of the locomotive was reflected in the increased load it hauled...'

Charles Lord interjected. 'That would be when the Stockton and Darlington Railway were in a bit of trouble...' He paused. 'Before they hit their stride,' he added as Joseph Pangborn carried on with his report back.

'It was Royal George that hauled them out of it. Blast pipe, return flue and the locomotive put on six wheels all in one huge step forward. Timothy Hackworth was obviously a man who knew what he was doing with locomotives.'

Charles Lord reminded himself of the mission they had set themselves. 'When I contacted the family I was sure there must be some evidence somewhere to back up the letter from George Stephenson to Timothy Hackworth. The one where he said he was using fans to get the draught. If George Stephenson had known or understood the blast-pipe, he would never have needed to do that.'

Major Pangborn had considered how valuable the help from Timothy Young had been. He started to tell Charles Lord so. 'I think you will find that the young Mr Hackworth...'

Instead of listening, Charles Lord recalled the starting point he and Joseph Pangborn had had. 'The blast pipe was such a simple and yet such a crucial piece of the puzzle in making steam locomotion viable. Do you know, it was sufficiently important there were reports put about that George Stephenson had stolen the idea from Hackworth. Even Robert Stephenson claimed it, first for his father, then for himself in Rocket the locomotive he built for the Rainhill Trials. That was before the all important letter you turned up.'

Joseph Pangborn now had a story to tell about such claims; one that went beyond the contents of letter. One that would please the man who had authorised the display of historic locomotives; their advent the starting point for the world to reach out to its neighbours in trade, travelling at greater speed than ever before. He continued. 'Well, we have it from the horses mouth. Correspondence from Hackworth's own son, from one of his drivers and the records to show that it was not so. Timothy Hackworth invented the blast-pipe, understood it and used it to good effect before anyone else. Stuffing the steam exhaust straight up the chimney, the way that others did, was never going to be enough to unleash the power of the locomotive. And in the end they all followed his lead.'

Charles Lord was gratified. Hopefully Pangborn had more for him. He smiled and sat back, waiting for what else might be brought to the table. Nothing was immediately forthcoming. He evidently needed prodding if the conundrum that taxed Charles Lord was to be resolved. 'I'm told, like others, we watched what was happening at Liverpool. And learnt from it. But we were also impressed with what was happening with the railway company that started it all. We kept close to the results from Stockton and Darlington, and they were making a success of their business where Liverpool and Manchester were facing difficulties. I hope you and young Mr Hackworth have more that could be said about the development of the Stockton and Darlington Railway and their superintendent than just the blast-pipe.'

He pulled out a leather bound report from the shelf behind his desk, turned to the appendices at the back, and read out for the benefit of Joseph Pangborn two quite different accounts of progress with the railways in England.

"This is from formal evidence given to the British Parliament. Firstly, from Henry Booth on behalf of the Liverpool and Manchester Railway. This is eight years after the opening. Eight years. Sufficient time you would have expected for them to have cleared away, got out from under, any early difficulties". He cleared his throat and read:

"The Liverpool and Manchester Railway, in reference to the formation of the road, and to all its moving machinery, is yet far from being completed. From the opening of the Railway to the present time, and more especially for the last 12 or 18 months, we have been in a state of transition, passing from the defective and imperfect, in form and construction, to more improved forms, and especially to increased strength in engines, coaches, and waggons."

Henry Booth had then proceeded to spell out the consequences for the railway.

"gradually these defects are in course of being remedied, but time and money are indispensable in this process, and the work of transition from wrong to right is far from being accomplished; further time will be needed, and further sums must be expended."

He turned over four or five pages before he continued. 'In clear contrast are the confident conclusions put forward, also in 1838, by Joseph Pease, director of the Stockton and Darlington Railway and MP.'

"The Stockton and Darlington Railway being the first of the kind (for public use and general traffic) cannot be taken as the best specimen; though I am not certain, as to its repair, management, and efficiency, or even public utility, that the Directors need yield the palm to any other party."

Joseph Pangborn had listened and was uncertain what to make of it. 'Whatever difficulties George Stephenson had encountered with the running of the Liverpool and Manchester Railway – and there were more than a few – he always pushed on through. Determined that the locomotive would prevail. That the vision he had of everyone using it, of it spreading and reaching across the whole country would become a reality. He was "Father of the Railway". His was the same spirit as Columbus; a man full of energy, self belief and an ambition that drove him on...'

The riposte was swift, definite not sharp. 'But Columbus's endeavour would never have got underway and succeeded without the ships on which he sailed across the world. Sounds to me as though Timothy Hackworth and the locomotives at Stockton and Darlington Railway were just as central to the success of the railway.'

And his further response was a considered one. Finance might not be Joseph Pangborn's strong point, but for Charles Lord it was always a measure of success and progress. 'For a start, the two railways were on a par in many ways. Similar number of locomotives in use. Comparable number of journeys being made with hauling goods. Returns to shareholders by way of dividends on the Stockton and Darlington were 8 per cent, and 9 per cent for Liverpool to Manchester. The share prices for both having risen, one from £100 to £300 and the other from £100 to £200 within its first four years. This was at a time when most railways were managing a bare one or two percent return to their shareholders, and some none at all.'

Such things, though not of concern to Joseph Pangborn, were bread and butter to Charles Lord's working life.

'Even so the two lines were different. Liverpool and Manchester were two commercial centres with a substantial and established trade. Merchandise and people were already being conveyed between the two cities. The mills were fed by the import of raw cotton, turned it into fabric and the result was exported to the world.'

Joseph Pangborn had a considerable grasp of the implications of transport. And well understood the comings and goings on trade routes between countries, not least America. 'Much of that cotton came from us...,' was the contribution he made in an attempt to retain the semblance of a conversation.

Charles Lord had a point to make. 'The original expectation and estimate in the Bill put before Parliament was that the Liverpool and Manchester Railway would take over all the existing traffic in goods, and they would provide the transport required by a few hundred passengers. In practice less than a third of the anticipated daily 4,500 tons of goods traffic passed on the railway, denting the projected revenue figures, but there were 400,000 passengers a year being carried at the equivalent of three times the price of hauling goods. Stephenson was saved from the increased competition of reduced prices on the canals and the stage coaches by the very profitable passenger traffic.

He looked directly at Joseph Pangborn, as he said, 'And the need for passengers was what brought us to you, do you remember?'

Joseph Pangborn vividly remembered the day he had met John Garrett, President of the Baltimore and Ohio Railroad. The man who realised that it would be passenger traffic as much as strong locomotives that would be the making of the B&O. Between them they had drummed up business – made excursions and trips on the train a part of what they had to offer the public. Then, he too had been caught in the spell of the locomotive, and stayed the course. Now he was intent on sharing it with the world through the historic display he had carved out for the railway he worked for.

Charles Lord's next comments brought him back to the business at hand. 'The Stockton and Darlington Railway on the other hand serviced the increasing number of coal mines that were being driven into the depths of the ground. Coal was the raw material under their feet, the mineral wealth of the region. It powered the Industrial Revolution and led them to establish two towns that didn't exist before: Shildon and Middlesborough.'

Charles Lord judged that that of itself was some unique achievement. 'And before those towns came into existence there wouldn't have been much call for passenger conveyance. It was previously 300 people a month until, after a few years of expanding trade, the passenger numbers came up to 10,000 a month, the same level at which the Liverpool and Manchester Railway had started.'

He was aware the development of the trade because of the Stockton and Darlington Railway was just as unique an achievement too. The financial case for the original Bill was based on the haulage of 10,000 tons of goods a year, with little allowance for passenger traffic. They hadn't taken a slice of existing trade to create their future. They had carved out an expansion of trade so significant that it changed the face of the whole North East of England. 'In practice, by the time the port at Middlesbrough was opened, it was capable of handling 4000 tons a day and had virtually monopolised the trade in the vicinity. That was a pioneering endeavour and I'm sure Timothy Hackworth was in the middle of it. There should be much that can be uncovered about those times.'

Joseph Pangborn had only too recently been on the receiving end of the diligence of Timothy Young's quest to uncover the achievements of his grandfather. He responded to Charles Lord's unstated question. 'Mr Timothy has been following the work of his grandfather... He has a welter of information he wants me to look at. I'm very conscious that Timothy Hackworth will be the first man that visitors will see when they come up to the

Inventors Gallery. Mr Timothy seems to be suggesting that Stockton and Darlington Railway under Timothy Hackworth's stewardship was step-by-step, easily moving forward... gearing up to meet demand as it arose. In comparison, he says, the Stephensons were, not to make too much of it, failing. Failing to deliver. Failing to live up to expectations.'

Charles Lord returned to his own pre-occupation. 'The puzzle I had, looking at the figures, was how the costs per mile on each railway were so different. One was three times the other. In the beginning, so far as I could see, it meant that hauling merchandise on the Liverpool and Manchester Railway was not paying its way, not making a profit. How, with the two major trade centres linked, could that be?'

Joseph Pangborn looked askance at that suggestion as Charles Lord carried on talking. 'The answer to that conundrum I believed had to lay with what Timothy Hackworth accomplished with the locomotive. Why? Because Timothy Hackworth had such confidence in his costs that he contracted to run the line and charge Stockton and Darlington Railway a fixed price; less than half a penny per ton per mile. And at that rate he would agree to provide for locomotives, drivers, fuel and repairs. All the while the level of traffic was increasing, as demand increased and yet more mineral wealth was unearthed. They were carrying three times the tonnage of goods of the Liverpool and Manchester Railway ... and charging a fraction of the price.'

That comment left Joseph Pangborn cold. Columbus had been driven by his ambition to find the way to a new world. Had he been mapping out the routes for locomotives to drive across countries, he would have had little concern about the effect it would have on the price of transporting coal. And George Stephenson, like Columbus, would have been pressing on regardless.

Charles Lord had by then brought the discussion to the path he wished to have followed. 'So I would be more than content to find your young Mr Hackworth had uncovered the answer to what puzzled me about those early times,' he said. Urging him on, he added, 'That's why I wanted him here. Find that, then you and young Mr Hackworth will have fulfilled my every expectation.'

Now was evidently the time for Major Pangborn to make use of what Timothy Young had uncovered. 'Of course Mr Timothy has been doing that. He has traced the developments his grandfather made in the locomotives he built. First with Royal George, then Sanspareil at the Rainhill trial, then swift engine Globe and heavy haulage with Wilberforce.'

'If that's the case, then your Mr Timothy is actually doing us all the great service I'd hoped for. I had this belief there had to be more to Timothy Hackworth than the blast-pipe. His inventiveness wouldn't have stopped there. His locomotives must have had a pioneering role to play and, I am determined, if we are to tell the history of the locomotive then we have to bring to the light of day his contribution. I was sure there was a story to be found. Hence my approach to the Hackworth family. Bringing in a family member, in this case his grandson, was key to uncovering with their help what we might have missed. If Mr Timothy can provide information for you about the development of the railway and locomotives at Stockton and Darlington Railway then find a way of telling that story.'

Joseph Pangborn thought he already had that in hand. 'We are standing Hackworth and Stephenson side by side in the Inventors Gallery, and they both have locomotives in the main display...'

Before Joseph Pangborn could complete the sentence, Charles Lord interrupted him. 'Joseph, I can't commend you enough for the celebration you have already created of early locomotives, and how our name stands at the fore. Well done indeed. If your display of locomotive history has our name to it, I do want justice done to the railway that was "first in the world", just as much as I want our standing as the "first in America" confirmed through the display you have put on.'

Charles Lord sat squarely upright, placed both his hands firmly on the desk. 'The gulf between the evidence given to the British Parliament for the Liverpool and Manchester and for the Stockton and Darlington Railways needs explaining. As does the confidence of Joseph Pease, more than ten years after the opening, in still placing the Stockton and Darlington Railway at the head of the queue for accolades. Until you find the answer to that question, Joseph, your work isn't finished.'

* * *

Major Joseph Pangborn retraced his steps, walked back past the Boardroom. Waiting for the lift, he realised he had let his own thoughts be swept aside by Charles Lord's concerns. Finding a home for the exhibits that had painstakingly been collected and put together was high on his agenda. He had wanted to float his idea of establishing a National Museum of Transportation, donated to the nation by the Baltimore and Ohio Railroad, with all the kudos that would attract. Time, though, to attend to more immediate matters. Arrangements had to be confirmed for his VIP guests at the opening in less than three weeks time, for the members of the press and for those who had worked so hard at Mount Clare Roundhouse to bring his idea to life.

As he descended to his office on the floor below, he gave his bushy moustache a twirl to keep it in order. Nothing could be left out of place. Certainly not George Stephenson. Nor Timothy Hackworth.

CHAPTER NINETEEN

All about two pioneers
at the Exposition

Exposition site, Wednesday 12th April 1893

Two men stood together in the cold Chicago spring
weather alongside the rails on which had been placed the
evidence. No-one who saw it could doubt that this was an
authentic reflection of pioneering progress. 'Samson' had
the attention of William Tranton, specially arrived from
Mount Clare Roundhouse to check that all was well with the
Baltimore and Ohio locomotives, and now easily diverted
to see one of the long-time heavyweight locomotives of its
time. The other man was George Davidson. His history
and connection with this locomotive went back to when
it was under construction. He had been one of Timothy
Hackworth's men in the Soho Works whose hand had
helped build this locomotive for the Albion Mines. A
man born of hardy north-of-England stock, he took little
persuading to travel with the locomotive when it was
transported to Canada, and even less persuading about
staying with it. He had been the first driver of 'Samson',
and that had been more than 50 years ago. Now 76 years
old, he took it as a privilege to accompany his locomotive to
the Exposition, and to be the one to lead it out for all to see.

Timothy Young had been beaten by them both to the first close up look at the veteran locomotive. It proudly still proclaimed its origins. There could be little doubt that it had been built by his grandfather. It looked for all the world like the images he had seen of Royal George. The same six wheels with their distinctive Hackworth design, the boiler extending beyond and a place at either end for driver and fireman, open to the elements. The wording of the metal plaque affixed to the side and below the boiler was still visible: SAMSON. He approached the elderly man, with what seemed like a hundred questions in his mind.

'Good morning. You have to be George Davidson.' The older man eyed him up and down as he continued speaking. 'I'm Timothy Hackworth Young, grandson of Timothy Hackworth and superintendent of this part of the Exposition,' he said by way of introduction. 'This was your locomotive?' he asked.

George Davidson's 'Oh, yes. She was mine for years. Never let me down,' was said with pride. 'Showed all the other drivers what a dependable powerhouse she was'.

William Tranton joined the conversation. 'Good morning, young Mr Hackworth. I told you at the workshops at Mount Clare that I could always recognise one of your grandfather's locomotives. And this one is still going strong. George was telling me about the hundreds of tons that she hauled at a time, and riding up steep hills with a hundred tons was never a problem.' He pointed to the long boiler and the framework perch with its controls through which the driver managed the running of 'Samson'. 'He also let me look at the workings. There are parts and bearings in there that show hardly any wear after forty years of almost constant use. Now you can see what I meant about always being able to tell a Hackworth locomotive. That's what you call engineering.'

George Davidson added, 'She's still in good working order. As good as the days when I was working on building her in your grandfather's Soho Works in Shildon. In all her forty years of working life there was hardly any call for repairs. She just went on, and on, and on. All weathers, all loads. And there's still life in her now. I can't wait to get her fired up. To get steam up once again. And William here is champing at the bit to help me.'

Timothy Young had followed what his grandfather had done, first through what the family had said, then the through the words of engineers. Now, here was a man who had been there, witnessed at first hand the practicalities of building locomotives. 'George, before you two do that, tell me. What was it like at Soho Works?'

'When I was there the works were brought on once your grandfather had the contract to keep the locomotives and all else in working order for the railway. It spread out over several acres. There was a foundry, the machine shop, a blacksmith's shop and an erecting shop that could house a number of locomotives being worked on.'

'And my grandfather. What was he like to work for?'

'He had more than 50 hands to manage. He was strict about doing a day's work for a day's pay. You could be fined for turning in late. But fair wages. And no work on Sundays. He was really strict about that.'

George Davidson took himself back to days of his youth in Shildon, when he had been taught so much. 'He was quite a man, your grandfather. He showed you how to do so many things. How to measure. How to calculate.

How to bend metal to your tune. How to turn the lathe. How to make each part of the locomotive well, so as to last long.' Timothy Hackworth had passed on his skill and experience to George Davidson, which made his life here in Canada a possibility, and even at this distance in time the gratitude was clear to see. 'You had to keep things in order, keep to your own tools. Above all he showed you how to do it right. And kept you to that standard. He set up the Railway Institute for all us workers. His apprentices were sought after. Many men, like me, went out from there and made their way in the world.'

Timothy Young took it all in. Now he'd seen for himself the size and power of 'Samson' and heard at firsthand how it was that his grandfather's locomotives could outlive and outperform others. Undoubtedly, his watchwords of 'Simplicity' and 'Economy' had been his guiding principles and drilled into every man that worked for him. So too were the essential elements of engineering competence. His legacy was as much the men who worked for him, the building of a town of locomotive workers, and the passing on of his skills, as it was constructing locomotives that hauled goods or passengers with equal ease.

William Tranton already had a definite view about the quality of Hackworth locomotives. He had the measure of their standing. 'Come on George, let's put her through her paces. The Superintendent here has work to do.'

Timothy Young left the two men to their preparations of 'Samson' for the opening of the Exposition, content in the knowledge that whatever else happened, an enduring tribute to the work of his grandfather was set to be lead locomotive, leading out from the front on the opening day parade.

They were right, he did indeed have other work that called for his attention. A letter from cousin Sam Holmes in New York urged him to look to the last of their grandfather's locomotives in order to complete the story of his work for the exposition. And Major Pangborn was due to return from Baltimore ready for the completion of the display for the Inventors Gallery. He walked back through the Transportation Annex, continued past the historic locomotives on show, then out through the magnificently decorated arches that formed the entrance of the Transportation Building and on to the neighbouring Administration Building.

Major Pangborn was still contemplating how to deal with Charles Lord's request. He had to hope that Timothy Young had the answers at his finger tips. Of course he would have. He had been diligent beyond the point that he required to complete the details of the Inventor's Gallery. More than the Major's reporter's instincts required. He had asked Timothy to meet him mid-morning in his office.

'Good morning, Timothy. We have yet to get to grips with the display for the Inventors Gallery. I had a discussion with Vice President Charles Lord yesterday. He's very pleased with the work we have done together, particularly impressed when I told him about your researches into the locomotives of the Stockton and Darlington Railway. He wants to make sure we do justice to them, "the first in the world" as he put it. He told me that one of their directors gave evidence that they were ahead of others for performance, and that an officer of the Liverpool and Manchester Railway didn't disagree.' The response he received was tempered by the serious consideration Timothy Young had given to the work of his grandfather and the railway whose interests he served.

'Well he was right. When I first came to look at how those two railways compared, they seemed on a par. Prices charged for their passenger journeys were similar. They were on a par for fuel consumption. Both were giving good and similar dividends to their shareholders, which spoke to their profitability.

'That I discovered was deceptive. It was not the whole story. The profits for Stockton and Darlington were produced from charging less than one-and-a-half pence per ton carried. On the other hand, Liverpool and Manchester were charging more than four pence per ton – accomplishing the 10s a ton price for carriage of goods between the two centres of trade they had promised. Stockton and Darlington Railway was looking to hold their running costs as low as possible, so they could reduce the cost of raw material they delivered, increase demand and expand their market. Liverpool and Manchester Railway were attacking an existing market. To be competitive they simply had to operate at a reduction of one third to existing prices. On those figures, who do you think was the more efficient?'

It was a question posed, but not one to which Timothy was expecting a response. He had already discovered that answer himself. And, now he was invited to, would pass on his conclusions to Major Pangborn.

'Pambour with his extensive experiments showed up the differences. It was in the costs. He looked at the amounts of money shown in the accounts of both railways, drawing a comparison between their running costs. When he calculated their costs as for each ton, for each mile carried, he found those on the Liverpool and Manchester Railway's were half as much again as on the Stockton and Darlington.' As a locomotive man Timothy had been surprised at what that finally pointed to.

'There was one very prominent difference between the running of the two railways. Repair costs. Repair costs are what marks out the locomotives of the two men, Timothy Hackworth and Robert Stephenson. You can hardly miss that in Pambour's work and his treatise.' The disruption that can cause was as much a concern to Timothy now, as a foreman for the Chicago, Milwaukee and St Paul Railroad, as it would have been then to anyone responsible for managing a railway.

'Repair costs for all twenty-three of the Stockton and Darlington locomotives in use at the end of 1833 were £1667. Repairs for the thirty locomotives on the Liverpool and Manchester Railway in the same six month period were £8783. However you look at it... not just that bald figure, but making allowance for the longer distance on the Liverpool line, or for the weights carried, even then there is a gulf between the two railways. Bluntly, Stephenson's locomotives needed substantially more repairs than those of Hackworth.'

Major Pangborn, not normally over concerned about the detail of the finances, had a sense of where Charles Lord's concerns had sprung from. He had, though, been asked to find answers about the work of the two pioneers, not more questions.

Timothy Young continued, 'Pambour provides the answer to that conundrum. Of the thirty locomotives provided to the Liverpool and Manchester Railway, ten were in service at one time, ten were in repair and the early locomotives were set aside.' He paused before he laid out for Major Pangborn the difficulties there had been in making progress on the Liverpool and Manchester Railway. 'Robert Stephenson unable to meet the requirements tried variation on variation as he produced the number of 'Rocket-style' locomotives ordered. The original Rocket locomotive had 25 tubes in the six feet long boiler and a cylinder of eight inches diameter. Couldn't have been sufficient, so the first one delivered to the Liverpool and Manchester Railway had 88 tubes, which was then increased to 92 in 'Arrow', a later locomotive. Next the cylinder size was increased, then he increased the length of the boiler, only by a further six inches but sufficient, in theory, to grab yet another five or ten per cent of steam power.' The Stephenson's triumph at Rainhill did not, Timothy had discovered, translate into immediate success.

The 'Northumbrian' was the last in the line and, fitted with 132 tubes, it must have been the epitome of what Robert Stephenson was searching for. He must have reached the physical limit of how many tubes he could fit into the boiler space, Timothy Young had realised. He also then, just as his grandfather had done with Royal George, adopted and used the diversion of exhausted steam to raise the temperature of the water. Even then, nothing went to plan on the Liverpool and Manchester Railway, and locomotives were having to help each other up the inclines.

Their locomotives had other failings to deal with. All the while the power was lacking, the tubes were also getting blocked and bursting. Timothy considered it must have been a dispiriting time for him.

None of which would have dampened the spirits of the passengers for whom the journey time between the two centres was cut in half, even if it was a bit of a slow 'chug chug' for the straining locomotives as they went up the inclines.

'So with the lack of sufficient power delivered by the locomotives, with the seams and joints and connections under stress, and with the bursts of tubes it was small wonder that the early locomotives were set aside,' Timothy said, before adding, 'and in any case, while the 'Rocket-type' locomotives could be worked together on the inclines so they could actually haul the five tons weight of the passengers each trip, their power was no match for the much greater weight of goods loads that were supposed to be carried.

The answer was the Planet locomotive that Robert Stephenson delivered, which had been needed as a matter of urgency. More powerful and a smoother steadier ride, he must have breathed a sigh of relief when he took the directors out and it successfully hauled 50 tons of varied merchandise and goods from Manchester to Liverpool. Albeit still needing assistance up the inclines, even though by then it had been fitted with a blast-pipe in similar manner to Hackworth's locomotives.'

'So, the Liverpool and Manchester Railway found their way through early teething problems then?' was the laconic comment from Major Pangborn, who had hoped to be able to sweep such difficulties for the Stephensons aside.

Timothy Young had to disappoint him. 'You might have expected the repair costs to fall as improvements were made, but not so. Colborn in his book has them not reducing but growing evermore; from just over 9 pence per mile in 1832, then to nearly 11 pence in 1833 and reaching 13 pence a mile one year later. His comments about the reflection this has on the quality of the workmanship are uncompromising. And in harsh economic terms, he points out that what was spent by the Liverpool and Manchester Railway in 1833 repairing their deficient locomotives, could instead have paid for twenty brand new locomotives.'

Timothy had found the inadequacies of the locomotives on the Liverpool and Manchester Railway went deeper. He added, 'And we have the observation of Henry Booth at the conclusion of the trial run for the Planet locomotive. He had said what was still needed was an altogether more powerful locomotive.'

Robert Stephenson had to resolve that shortcoming. The result was Goliath, with 14-inch cylinders and coming in at 10 tons, the first of two locomotives that became known as the bank engines; locomotives with the power to haul goods. And finally he adopted the six wheels used by Hackworth in his design of heavy duty locomotives, gaining traction, spread of weight load on the rails and stability.

Timothy Young had a more upbeat and satisfactory story to tell Major Pangborn when it came to the Stockton and Darlington Railway. 'Meanwhile, my grandfather had things under control. Under his control. He was building locomotives on his own account without having to involve Robert Stephenson and Co, only to be slowed down by them or having his ideas plundered.' He caught the look on Major Pangborn's face. 'Maybe that is too harsh, but he was certainly meeting the demands of the Stockton and Darlington Railway on his own and taking them in his stride. Including the passenger traffic which, with the advent of Middlesbrough, was considerably increased.'

Timothy Young paused before bringing the work of his grandfather into focus. 'The locomotives Timothy Hackworth constructed, unlike those of others, continued to stay the distance, whether they were for the traffic of goods or of passengers. 'Samson' that stands outside is the very demonstration of all that was to be found in Hackworth locomotives, Joseph: power, quality of construction, economy and durability. And the final proof, if that is still needed, lay with their repair costs. They were three-and-a-half pence per mile. One third of those of the Liverpool and Manchester Railway.' Timothy Young had grown to understand for himself how much his grandfather had given to the locomotives that established the railways. 'Timothy Hackworth knew what had to be delivered, knew how to deliver it, and understood how to maintain and sustain it.'

It wasn't only on that count that he needed to honour the memory of his grandfather. Timothy Hackworth had stepped forward to take on a task just as challenging to all his abilities as anything that George Stephenson had contemplated in driving through the line of the railway for the Liverpool and Manchester Railway.

He had once again backed up his judgment and laid on the line all his know-how, skill and experience with the locomotive.

Timothy Young completed the picture for Major Pangborn. 'My grandfather was never one to offer empty promises. His word counted. He reached an agreement to run the railway for the Stockton and Darlington Railway.

He took over the running, the staffing, the repairs and the servicing of the capital cost of the locomotives; all that for the rate of less than a fraction of a penny a mile per ton. He was good to his word. From a director of Stockton and Darlington, the observation was made that there had never been a more powerful locomotive than Hackworth's and that all they needed were more like it. It was an economy of running a railway that has rarely been matched since.'

The contrast between the two railways that he had uncovered had been clear to see. 'While my grandfather ran a steady ship for the Stockton and Darlington Railway, on the Liverpool and Manchester Railway they were in a continual scramble. Science of the time and cold logic failed Robert Stephenson at every turn he made. He was shooting arrows in the dark. The words he had used in his response to the report of Walker and Rastrick came back to haunt him; as he had said, the fruits of direct experience of running a railway was always the better measure of what could be accomplished than the speculations fine words could argue for. The only man who had that combined experience, inventiveness and the practical skills was Timothy Hackworth.'

The two pioneering railways, Timothy Young found, were quite different in what they accomplished. The Liverpool and Manchester Railway was originally looking to bring to the railway an overwhelming percentage of the existing business of the canals and the roads. They had increased their figures from 106,000 tons at the introduction of the service to 138,000 by the end of 1833, but it was still only one third of the total business between the two trading centres.

'The truth, Joseph, is that for Liverpool and Manchester Railway it was the lucrative passenger service that was their route to prosperity. It had started at an unexpected 445,000 passengers and subsequently held steady at around 400,000. All else was a costly uphill struggle, despite ideas that were borrowed from my grandfather.'

He added, 'Meanwhile, the Stockton and Darlington Railway was leading the way and steadily expanding its business. The goods hauled had, by 1833, increased fourfold from the 110,000 tons carried in 1828 to 420,000 tons; a figure that the Liverpool and Manchester Railway were expected to haul but never managed to acquire. Stockton and Darlington extended the reach of the railway from the original 25 miles of track as it incorporated links to more and more coal mines and took up more and more traffic. It was also benefiting from a growing but modest level of passenger traffic, rising from virtually nothing to 12,000 a month, one third of that on the Liverpool and Manchester Railway. My grandfather lived up to his word, delivering passenger and goods traffic on a double line with powerful locomotives and with swift locomotives, exactly as he predicted was possible. And the Stockton and Darlington Railway prospered.'

Timothy Young had indeed reached his own conclusion about how far the words of Mr Hackworth reached. The difference between the two men had brought home to Timothy Young how accomplished a locomotive engineer his grandfather had been. Hackworth with his locomotives had the measure of the railway. Robert Stephenson, by all that he had struggled to master, never quite measured up.

He was indeed able to offer Major Pangborn an answer to Charles Lord's question. 'It was the power of Timothy

Hackworth's locomotives that delivered economy of purpose to the Stockton and Darlington Railway. It was the Stockton and Darlington Railway, above all others, that gave birth to and cradled the development of the railway. In terms of setting the standard for locomotion Timothy Hackworth, and the railway he devoted his energy to, stood tall. Exactly as you heard from Charles Lord. Ten years after the opening of the Stockton and Darlington Railway, and seven years after the arrival of the Liverpool and Manchester Railway, they had no reason to hand the palm to anyone else.'

Major Pangborn had a simpler view of what had happened. 'The Liverpool and Manchester Railway got there in the end, though. I understood that Robert brought together all the design features he had harnessed in his pursuit of power from his locomotives; amalgamated them to define a patentable locomotive – not very imaginatively called 'Patentee'. Then that was put forward for the all lines he was involved with. Whereas, word of the performance of Hackworth's locomotives and his achievements for the railway weren't heard about much beyond the confines of the Stockton and Darlington Railway.'

'Well. Isn't that exactly what you wanted of me?' Timothy Young replied. 'To bring together what the family knew, and combine that with the reports and all the speculations from over the years? To make the record clear?' And, Timothy thought, it had become clear.

'Now I can tell you how it was that the Stockton and Darlington Railway was the birthplace and cradle of the railways of the world. Then how it expanded to become the backbone of the industry that was created in its wake.' There was a touch of indignation in his voice as he continued. 'I have found my grandfather put Stockton and Darlington ahead of the Liverpool and Manchester Railway and kept them there during his time as superintendent. Aren't we supposed to be setting the record straight? To tell the world all about the contributions he made? Giving Timothy Hackworth his true place in the history of the development of the locomotive?'

Timothy Young had brought with him the Memoir of his grandfather that he had found among the family papers. A memoir to celebrate the life of his grandfather, compiled by those who knew him. Timothy Young when he had first come across the Memoir celebrating the work and times of Timothy Hackworth, a document of tributes, had looked with admiration at the list of the inventions. The sheer variety, as he had tackled the development and overcome the difficulties of working the Stockton and Darlington line, was impressive as was the description by Uncle John of their significance. He faced Major Pangborn with the evidence.

'Joseph, if there was any doubt as to what my grandfather invented it's here.' Timothy turned to the back of the pamphlet to show Major Pangborn the extent of the works and inventions attributed to the skill of Timothy Hackworth. There along with the blast-pipe and Royal George, more than twenty steps forward in the development of the locomotive were listed.

Major Pangborn saw Hackworth's invention of the blast-pipe and the locomotive Royal George as central to what he contributed to the history of the locomotive but momentarily was overwhelmed by the scope of Hackworth's other work. It was just as important for him to give recognition to the importance of George Stephenson in what they did. He tempered Timothy's comments with his own. 'The inventive faculty, indeed, is only rarely found united with tenacity of purpose, determined energy, and self-belief. Just like Columbus, George Stephenson had that when he persevered against the odds to make the Manchester and Liverpool Railway a reality.'

Here for Major Pangborn was the balance between the endeavours and triumphs of the two men. 'Stephenson used the Stockton and Darlington Railway as his springboard. The world had never seen the likes of that before. The public were left in awe. And merchants, shareholders and the public who witnessed and enjoyed the fruits of the Liverpool and Manchester Railway made his reputation as "Father of the Railway".

And, Pangborn had considered, there was good reason for that title 'He remained the one man in England who had experience of building railways, railways designed to be used by steam locomotives. His was the accepted know-how. What he said was right, not to be gainsaid.'

Major Pangborn had given considerable thought as to how he would portray George Stephenson. It was time to share those thoughts with Timothy Young. 'He carried forward the Bolton and Leigh Railway. He pushed on with plans for the next major railway connection. The ambitious 112 miles of a route from Birmingham to London. That occupied him, even while he was engaged with the construction of the Liverpool to Manchester. And the piece of the puzzle that would make it all make sense – the connecting Grand Junction Railway. His vision was for the railways to reach across the whole country.

He also had the contacts and support to bring that about. The influence of the Quakers, the bankers and the Unitarian merchants of Liverpool and Manchester were as significant a part of getting the money behind the projects as was getting Parliamentary consent. The confidence they had in him stemmed not from his technical competence but from the virtual guarantee that with his energy and commitment their investments would be rewarded and profits would roll in...'

Major Pangborn had found that George Stephenson was there at every turn. He was always in demand – as engineer, as surveyor, as consultant. He was engaged with so many railways. Major Pangborn looked to his notebook and, for Timothy Young's benefit, reeled off the additional names.'...there was the North Midland between Derby and Leeds, the York and North Midland from Normanton to York, the Manchester and Leeds, the Birmingham and Derby, the Sheffield and Rotherham. Bills were passed in Parliament authorising the construction of an additional 214 miles.'

Major Pangborn looked up. 'There was so much to do that a secretary travelled with him by post-chaise on the road, taking notes, writing letters, setting out observations and proposals. I was told they travelled more than twenty thousand miles in that time, even though six months of it were spent in London.'

In the face of such a catalogue of accomplishments Timothy Young quailed at the thought of what energy it must have taken. This from a man who at 56 was no longer in his prime. 'Wasn't he taking on too much?'

'Perhaps – then so too did Columbus,' was Major Pangborn's response. 'It meant, when he came to give evidence to a House of Commons Committee later he could say with some justification, "There is hardly a railway in England that I have not had to do with." And he had a hand in railways abroad too.'

Timothy Young was not to be deterred. 'But first, the locomotive had needed my grandfather's inventiveness and skill and sheer understanding to prosper and serve as a touchstone for all that followed. Taking his locomotives at Stockton and Darlington altogether he played a singular and defining part in the history of the locomotive. There can surely be no doubting the importance of his contribution. Although I do have to concede that no man contributed so much as George Stephenson to the establishment of the modern railway system.'

'None of that progress was easy,' Pangborn confirmed. 'Not every one of the railways that were built was a resounding financial success. Out of a list of forty railways I looked at a considerable number were paying an unconvincing dividend of 1, 2 or 3 per cent, or no dividend at all. Which with their consistently high returns, set the Liverpool and Manchester and the Stockton and Darlington Railways apart. Not just by being the first, but together setting the stamp on the locomotive as a means of transport, transforming the face of the world.'

Aware that time was pressing, he concluded with, 'In which case we have to make sure they share the honours in the inventors gallery. Set out in a way in the Inventors Gallery that is not beyond the public's comprehension. I'll leave that concern with you. We'll come back to this tomorrow, and finalise the layouts for the displays then.'

Back in his office, Timothy Young pondered Major Pangborn's words about how best to tell the story of the pioneers who set the pace, pressed the locomotive engine into service of the world at large. His grandfather stood out among the crowd. He picked up the memoir that Aunt Prudence had sent him, to remind himself how much. There was far more to his life than Royal George. Sam Holmes most recent letter had confirmed for him that developing the locomotives for the Stockton and Darlington Railway had become Timothy Hackworth's work after the Rainhill Trials. And nowhere did he fall short. In his letter cousin Sam had pointed to yet more of their grandfather's achievements. There was another locomotive to add to the growing list of his grandfather's accomplishments. A further tribute to his engineering prowess.

NEW YORK AND PACIFIC STEAMSHIP, COAL
AND LUMBER COMPANY.

DIRECT STEAMSHIP LINE
BETWEEN
NEW YORK AND PACIFIC COAST.
MONTHLY SAILINGS.

MORRIS BUILDING,
64, 66 & 68 BROAD STREET.

SAMUEL HOLMES, General Agent.
Cable Address: Holmes, New York.
Watkins & Scott's 10th Edition Codes.
Telephone Call: 1010 Broad.

NEW YORK, 10 April 1893

Dear Timmy,

Grandfather did just that. He remained building locomotives for the Stockton and Darlington Railway. Building more and more locomotives as the traffic increased, at times his designs were let out for other locomotive engineers to build them.

There was a crowning glory. A triumph in performance and a pace setter in engineering skill. One with which Uncle John challenged the Stephensons to a trial pitted against the best they had, to determine who had the superior locomotive. That gauntlet was never picked up.

Grandfather's last engine was the "Sanspareil No. 2." Completed in 1849. This engine you will find elaborately featured and illustrated in the Practical Mechanics Journal, Nos. 25, 26, 27 and 29, April, May, June and August, 1850. It was said at the time of its appearance, "No locomotive has yet been produced that will compete with it as a piece of workmanship."

All the longitudinal seams in the barrel of the boiler were welded, instead of riveted. I watched the operation of welding the seams, and can say grandfather gave it his personal attention and direction. The angles were welded on the ends of the barrel and turned to a truth in the lathe for receiving the smoke and fire boxes. Portions of the latter were welded instead of riveted. When this engine came out of the erecting shop under steam, I was on her. In experimental trial trips, this engine attained a speed of 80 miles an hour.

It represented the culmination of his lifetime of building locomotives, as he said in a letter to a prospective purchaser. "I would just add, I have had to do with the locomotive from its commencement, a period of thirty-nine years, and

NEW YORK AND PACIFIC STEAMSHIP, COAL AND LUMBER COMPANY
MORRIS BUILDING, 64, 66 & 68 BROAD STREET NEW YORK
Cable Address: Holmes, New York

perhaps some of the most startling improvements in the locomotive engine have originated with me."

In all his life, no-one doubted his word and those are not words of vain-glory such as others might proffer. That is a positive statement on this great question; of who is the Father of the Locomotive Steam Engine? It is uttered by grandfather himself, who was the chief worker in the period of the Locomotive's birth. The great engineer, from first to last, supported by unimpeachable proof, but by nothing stronger than his word.

Now that takes you through all that I know of grandfather's inventive spirit: 'Royal George', 'Sanspareil' No. 1 & No. 2, 'Globe', 'Wilberforce' and the mighty 'Samson'. Do the family proud, Timmy. We are all looking to you, to show the visitors from across the globe that Timothy Hackworth was one of the great founding fathers of Railway Locomotion.

SH

NEW YORK AND PACIFIC STEAMSHIP, COAL AND LUMBER COMPANY
MORRIS BUILDING, 64, 66 & 68 BROAD STREET NEW YORK
Cable Address: Holmes, New York

CHAPTER TWENTY

For all the world to see

Exposition site, the following day

Major Pangborn had collected together the material he expected to use alongside the portrait of George Stephenson. That part of his job was complete. In the simplest way he wanted to bring together, for each image of the man that the visitors would see, a focus on their work and accomplishments. Like the portraits that had been painted of distinguished men in the 18th Century, surrounded by images that spoke of their interests, signified their position and pointed to their wealth. The displays for George Stephenson would give the setting of the two major railways, show Locomotion, his, the first locomotive on the Stockton and Darlington Railway, the first public railway. Rocket, the declared winner at Rainhill, would need to stand out. Perhaps a diagram and a simple description since the replica was already standing in the annex on the floor below. He had considered reaching back in history to Killingworth but the reporter's brain told him there was only so much that the public would take in at a time. Better to have some 'headline' sight which they would remember than a mass and blur of a multitude of facts which would be lost to them the minute they walked on to the thing that caught their attention next.

Timothy Young had been taking in the sweep of all that could be brought to the attention of the public about his grandfather. The memoir included a reprint of 'A chapter in the History of Railway Locomotion' from an earlier copy of 'Practical Mechanics Journal', followed by a personal 'Memoir', a record of his Inventions and a letter from the executor of his will, Thomas Greener. Uncle John had brought out the detail of the 40 listed inventions in a further nine pages of notes.

Besides the locomotives that Timothy had become aware of there, there were his other inventive contributions to the running of the Stockton and Darlington Railway. The list included the simplest of practical expediencies – his 'Sledge Brake' for passenger carriages on steep gradients – the most bold advances – his 'Trunk Engine' with its forty-inch cylinder and thirty-inch stroke – and the sophisticated arrangements for the staithes and plans for a wrought iron bridge to carry the railway over the river Tees. All this besides the twenty specific advances he visited on the locomotives he designed and constructed.

Each of his grandfather's locomotives established itself as a practical accomplishment, incorporating distinctive and decided improvements. He remained in a class of his own during those formative years of the locomotive, contributing more than the stepping stone that had been the Royal George and the enduring and essential blast-pipe.

Timothy Young had also noted what Colborn had written:

'Hackworth's engine with 11–inch cylinders and a 20-inch stroke, was a bold departure from the practice of the period where a proportion of three times the bore of the cylinder appears to have been generally considered forty years ago, as indispensable; its maker thus led the way in respect of one of the most important proportions of the modern locomotive.'

In his own words, Timothy Hackworth had been "with the locomotive from its commencement, a period of thirty-nine years, and perhaps some of the most startling improvements in the locomotive engine have originated with me." Timothy Young looked at the record of achievements. He was indeed, as had been claimed, the "Father of Locomotives".

Major Pangborn opened the door to the office of Timothy Young, and breezed in. He had given further thought to the way the lives of the two locomotive engineers could best be depicted. They needed it resolved. He hoped that Timothy Young had too. He held the key to the accomplishments of his grandfather.

'Good morning, Timothy. Time to arrange the last outstanding item for us. The content of the displays by the portraits of our two pioneers: George Stephenson and Timothy Hackworth. Clear some space on that large table of yours. We need plenty of room to work on.'

'Joseph, while I do that I'd like you to take a good look through the Memoir of my grandfather. I think there is material there we can draw on. Particularly the Appendix that's annotated by my Uncle John.'

Major Pangborn took the proffered pamphlet, thinking it unlikely that such a slender document would carry much weight in their deliberations. He drew up a chair and sat down besides Timothy's rolltop desk. He opened and read while Timothy moved the stacks of magazines, piles of books and files of correspondence onto one side of the table.

He rapidly ran through the first pages, waiting for some aspect or thought about the life of Hackworth to stand out. They were all the fine words you would expect in such a document, with references to the Stockton and Darlington Railway and to Royal George, and to the correspondence from George Stephenson to Timothy Hackworth that had persuaded him about the origins of the blast-pipe. He did though stop and read more slowly and carefully the final pages, taking in the extensive details of the inventions. He had just begun to read a letter that seemed to summarise it all, when Timothy returned from his task.

Seeing Major Pangborn at that crucial part of the Memoir seemed the ideal point to open the discussion in the way he wanted. 'I'm not sure where we start, Joseph.' The letter from cousin Sam Holmes had urged him on, and today he was galvanised into action on behalf of his grandfather as Joseph Pangborn was about to discover. 'You can see for yourself. Timothy Hackworth, my grandfather, was original, actually of himself improving the locomotive in essentials as no other man was doing.' Major Pangborn rested the pamphlet on the desktop and looked up as Timothy continued with story he wished to have told about his grandfather.

'He was incomparably in advance of George Stephenson in everything which may be truly said to lay claim to distinction. Judge by the practical results following his efforts, he stamped a character upon the structure of the locomotive of the greatest significance.'

Major Pangborn sat back into the chair. He was happy to support Timothy in any way he could to be sure the visitors to the exposition had the story of the essentials of the development of the locomotive laid before them. But the role of George Stephenson was not to be set to one side. 'Timothy, in positions gained by the sheer force of his indomitable will, George Stephenson has been largely instrumental in compelling the consideration of the locomotive and set it on the railways. On railway after railway. That was his strength. That was his mastery. That made him "Father of the Railways"'.

'From what I have seen, Joseph, his early projects relative to the locomotive have been without practical or enduring value. Unlike my grandfather, he is not actually the inventor of any essential part of the locomotive engine. He only made progress by adopting the plans and suggestions of others. George Stephenson's capacity to successfully apply them is an achievement, but there is no essential which owes its origin to him. It is difficult to say in what respect any inventiveness on his part actually improved the structure or working of the locomotive.'

Timothy Young was intent on bringing his grandfather's work to light. He had uncovered locomotive developments that continued well beyond Royal George. Developments that he used to give the Stockton and Darlington Railway an untroubled future. 'My grandfather was the one setting the standard first. His innovations and the quality of work propelled their locomotives, whether it was a capacity of hauling goods or the speedier, lighter, load of passengers.

He understood that each required different things from the steam locomotive. Technically he added the blast-pipe, the preheating, the distinctive wheels, the coupling,..

Major Pangborn picked up the pamphlet he had laid on the desktop and scanned the pages he had been looking at. As Timothy listed them, he counted off the inventions and improvements that were a matter of record. Beyond Royal George there were four other locomotives, each of which contributed something new in the improvement of the locomotive by actually solving a problem that stood in the way of progress.

Timothy had continued,'..and his locomotives stayed on the line, working without breakdowns and needing few repairs, and working long years. The Stockton and Darlington Railway might not have had the prominence that its cousin the other side of the country enjoyed, but it ran efficiently because of those locomotives, created trade, built two new towns and unleashed the raw materials for the foundries...'

Major Pangborn sensed the determination. His instincts about involving the Hackworth family in making this, his account of the history of the locomotive, complete, had not let him down. There was a limit though to what could be accomplished through any displays in the Inventors Gallery. "You've persuaded me. Timothy Hackworth needs greater recognition than I had first planned. It is not just the two railways that share the honours; it is these two men who are standing side by side in the gallery.'

'Well, if George Stephenson was acclaimed as "Father of the Railways", then we have to give Timothy his rightful title too, that of "Father of the Locomotive".'

Titles are one thing, thought Major Pangborn. That's easily dealt with. A small plaque affixed to the frame of their portraits will see the two 'Fathers' side by side. Less easy to resolve was going to be the extent of the displays. Timothy Young looked to want a complete biography of his grandfather on display. The reporters experience would need to be used to telling effect.

'Timothy, in telling a story sometimes less is more – there is only so much the public will take in. What is needed is sufficient of a headline that will stay with them as they pass on by display after display.' He was reminded of the experience they had both had. 'Think about what we saw in the Fine Arts building. The different sorts of arts on display stayed with us – the pottery, the sculptures, the drawings, the paintings. But there came a point where after a few paintings they became not only of a mass altogether but less memorable individually.'

Timothy Young, recalling the visit, nodded his head in acceptance of the truth Major Pangborn had spelled out. He could remember each of the locomotives on display in the annex. That was because it was part of his job. But there was only one painting that had stayed with him after their visit: 'Sunflowers' by Claude Monet. And just one sculpture he could recall in any detail – the group of bullfighters in their distinctive costumes.

Major Pangborn continued, 'The gallery is to give our visitors just five faces to hang their experience on. Overload them with display after display of material and they will have forgotten it by the time they leave the building. Treat what we put on display about your grandfather as headline material. Give them two or three strong visuals to keep in their mind. We have to portray the impact of one man who is inventive and works with locomotives, the other is our Columbus – pushing out from early beginnings to make railways and passenger traffic in his mould.'

Major Pangborn reached out for the headline moments of Timothy Hackworth. The pioneering developments that established his position as first in the line of the pioneers. 'What marks out Timothy Hackworth as first and foremost?' was a reporter's question aimed at drawing out the significant part of an unfolding event.

'You mean Royal George and the blast-pipe?'

Major Pangborn already had the importance of Timothy Hackworth's contribution to the development of the locomotive clearly in his mind. 'Something more perhaps,' he said, with the crucial part of the development of the whole railway in mind. 'In spite of what George Stephenson had managed to include in the Parliamentary Bill, I mean saving the Stockton and Darlington from giving up, from turning back from the locomotive.'

'What about everything else he did? It won't be his story without...'

Pangborn also had a different take on the way the Hackworth story could be told. 'Timothy, remember the position you have. You will have visitors in the palm of your hand. What they see with their eyes, you can add to with what they hear from your voice– and those memories will stay long after they have left the building, left the Exposition itself. The words of the grandson of Timothy Hackworth, telling the story of his locomotives will be ringing in their ears, a once in a lifetime experience.'

It dawned on Timothy how he could do what the family could only have dreamt of doing. He had through working here found for himself all that was needed to be able to shine a light on Timothy Hackworth, for him to come out from the shadows. This was an opportunity the family would not have come to any other way. Instead of fighting to be heard among the clamour of voices of dissent in England, here he would have an audience eager to hear what he had to say about his grandfather.

'And that would be every day for the six months the Exposition is open wouldn't it?'

'Yes. There'll be no other opportunity like this.' Major Pangborn envisaged the advantage there would be for Timothy. 'A willing audience, an international audience. Not only locomotive engineers but the whole swathe of the public at large.'

'So what do you think we should make of the displays by their portraits?'

'I was going to bring the two railways George Stephenson worked for into prominence and his two locomotives – Locomotion and Rocket. Maybe something about the building of the Liverpool and Manchester Railway.'

'So for my grandfather we would do the same? Set out a map of the Stockton and Darlington line between their two portraits...,' was Timothy's pensive response.

'And we could add the details of his locomotives,' Major Pangborn suggested. 'The one's you mentioned you wanted to include: Royal George, Globe, Wilberforce. We already have Sanspareil on show with its history.'

Timothy Young was still trying to take it all in. Still wanted something to show how his grandfather stood out from the crowd.

Major Pangborn had that in hand. 'We still want a show stopper. A 'head of the bill' notice. I saw there was a brief account in a letter at the back of the Memoir. That would be a start. Plus reference to the blast pipe. And to how he saved the finances of the Stockton and Darlington Railway.'

'So we feature the locomotives on the Stockton and Darlington Railway– for both of them. And the railway itself, the Stockton and Darlington as it grew and expanded.'

'Timothy, leave that with me,' Pangborn said. 'Let me take the Memoir with me. I'll make something of it and come back to you, say in an hour. ...' A reporter's life of deadlines and headlines was never far away from the man. '...Then we are done.'

In his mind it was all settled, and Timothy Young, for his part, was charged up with the prospects.

Major Pangborn was true to his word. Faced with a letter to the papers, one he discovered that already said much of what was needed, he quite speedily arrived at the key part of the display for Timothy Hackworth.

He put a line through the first two lengthy paragraphs. They set the scene, but didn't set the direction for the piece. The third paragraph established the starting point with its "The first public railway was the Stockton and Darlington, opened September 27th, 1825." The word 'first' was in italics. Never one to understate the case, he instinctively changed that to capitals. The words "The FIRST railway.." caught the reader's attention. He would save any italics for phrases in the text that he wanted to emphasise.

The next paragraph in a few sentences already set out the background and impact of Royal George, including the invention by Timothy Hackworth of the blast-pipe. Nothing needed altering. It was as clear and concise a piece of writing as he might have crafted himself.

The fifth paragraph set up the letter from George Stephenson to Hackworth that demonstrated he had no comprehension of the possibility of such a device or its value. He put that to one side for the time being. Next came the quote from the book by Smiles, describing the attributes of the man who 'invented such a locomotive as made railway locomotion practicable and profitable'. From what Timothy Young had uncovered that fitted his grandfather like the proverbial glove.

That was followed by details of the improvements in the shares and the reduction in costs when Hackworth ran the line, as compared to those of the Liverpool and Manchester Railway. That told the story well enough. The last part of that final paragraph needed a bit of tidying up.

The headline to all these words was needed. It would have to place Timothy Hackworth ahead of George Stephenson. A simple headline was all that was required: 'GEORGE STEPHENSON'S LETTER to TIMOTHY HACKWORTH' sitting above a copy of the letter that confirmed Stephenson was using fans to provide the draught for combustion of the fuel.

Below that he would set an image of Royal George, centred with Hackworth's name to one side and, to the other, the locomotive's name and number.

He drafted a display that brought together all of Timothy Hackworth's pioneering work with locomotives and returned with it and the Memoir, from where he had taken the original letter, to Timothy Young.

Timothy Young looked over the material that was destined to tell the world the story of his grandfather. He listened as Pangborn explained what he had done. 'The headlines above, and below the 'blast-pipe' letter sets out the background for Hackworth's most important invention. The drawing of Royal George, with the date below showing it ahead of that of the letter, is an image that will get the attention of the visitor and draw them in...,' he said, 'to the text.' Adding, 'the concluding lines need a bit more work. What do you think?'

Timothy Young could not help but be impressed. Joseph Pangborn had found a way of describing the work of his grandfather that was beyond him. The last line was a step too far, to be expected given who the author of the letter was. The phrase 'incontrovertibly prove the author of the locomotive and railway system to have been Timothy Hackworth', claimed too much. His grandfather might be 'Father of the Locomotive' but to stretch it to include the railway system would be to deny George Stephenson all that he was entitled to.

Pangborn continued. 'I have removed a gratuitous downplaying of William Hedley. Not needed, distracted the reader from your grandfather who, after all, is the centre of attention in this piece. And I couldn't determine who the author of the letter was. Do you know who WYLAM is?'

'Oh yes. That is the name under which Uncle John wrote to the papers and journals. That would be John Wesley Hackworth, son of Timothy Hackworth.'

'Thank God you knew that. We ought to attribute the copyright to him, seeing as how we are using his words. If the world at large is going to see this then we had better do it right, don't you think. Thank you, Timothy.'

'I think you could do with changing the very last sentence. I assume your idea is to lay out the impact of my grandfather's work. Whatever he is 'the author of' it surely can't be said to be both 'the locomotive and the railway system'. I don't want to be as wrong about this as Smiles was about the sagacity of Mr Hackworth.'

Major Pangborn had a thought. He might be able to kill two birds with one stone. 'I said we wanted to do justice to your grandfather. Leave it with me, Timothy.'

Inventors Gallery Two weeks later

Major Pangborn had completed the display for George Stephenson, exactly as he had previously intended. There was a diagram that showed the route of the Liverpool and Manchester Railway. Picked out and identified were each of the main sections: Olive Mount Cutting, Chat Moss, the Sankey Viaduct, the Skew Bridge. So too was an engineering drawing of Rocket and, since the locomotive was actually on show in the annex, a brief account describing the workings of the multi-tubular boiler. He had also acquired a painting that showed the arduous workings of Mount Olive. Separately he had a schedule of the many other railways that George Stephenson either had under his direction or about which he had acted as consultant engineer.

Bringing together George Stephenson and Timothy Hackworth would be through their shared honours for the Stockton and Darlington Railway. Set out to the side of George Stephenson was a map of the line as it had been when it opened. Alongside Timothy Hackworth was another, showing the extended lines to the additional mines, and the towns of Darlington, Shildon, Stockton and including Middlesborough. Separately a schedule, description and outline of Hackworth's pioneering locomotives that powered the Stockton and Darlington Railway: Royal George, Globe and Wilberforce.

Timothy Hackworth Young drew himself up to his full Hackworth height as he looked at the portrait of his grandfather and the contents of the display cabinet that brought justice to the man and to his pioneering work. The headline, the 'blast-pipe' letter written in a classic hand that was set below and the image of Royal George were indeed altogether an arresting sight. The words underneath gave substance to the man who was 'Father of the Locomotive':

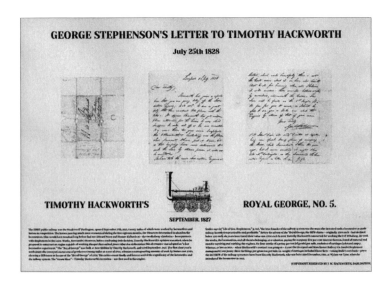

GEORGE STEPHENSON'S LETTER TO TIMOTHY HACKWORTH

July 25th 1828

TIMOTHY HACKWORTH'S ROYAL GEORGE, NO. 5.

SEPTEMBER 1827

He read first of all the part of the text setting out the circumstances that led to Royal George being constructed. Then followed an account of how it turned the tide in favour of the locomotive, and of his grandfather's crucial contribution.

"The FIRST public railway was the Stockton & Darlington, opened September 27th, 1825, twenty miles of which were worked by locomotives and horses in competition. The horses proving much more economical during the first eighteen months, the Directors determined to abandon the locomotives, (this would have resulted long before had not Edward Pease and Thomas Richardson – the two Railway chieftains – been partners with Stephenson in the Loco. Works, Newcastle.) However, before confirming their decision, Timothy Hackworth's opinion was asked, when he proposed to construct an engine capable of working cheaper than animal power.

After due deliberation this alternative was adopted as *"a last locomotive experiment."* The "Royal George" was built at New Shildon by Timothy Hackworth, and tried September, 1827. The first clear year's work (1828) she conveyed 22,412 tons of goods over twenty miles at a cost of £466, whereas a corresponding amount of work by horses cost £920, showing a difference in favour of the "Royal George" of £532. This achievement finally and forever settled the expediency of the locomotive and the railway system. The "steam blast" – *Timothy Hackworth's invention* – was first used in this engine."

Next came the reference to Samuel Smiles, and the confirmation that his grandfather's locomotive was the salvation of the Stockton and Darlington Railway. Following which he had then taken on responsibility for the running of the railway, at a fraction of the costs that George Stephenson had achieved.

"Smiles says in "Life of Geo. Stephenson," p. 167, *"the true founder of the railway system was the man who invented such a locomotive as made railway locomotion practicable and profitable."* Before the advent of the "Royal George", the S&DR shares – originally £100 each – had declined below £50 each, six years later (1833) their value was £300 each.

In 1833, Timothy Hackworth contracted for working the S&D Railway. He took the works, the locomotives, and all thereto belonging, at a valuation, paying the company five per cent interest thereon, found all material and men for repairing and working the engines, for *four-tenths* of a penny per ton (of *goods*) per mile, exclusive of carriages laden and empty. Whereas, as late as 1834, – when Hackworth's contract was going on – it cost the Liverpool and Manchester Railway Co. (under Stephenson management) *one penny three farthings* per *gross* ton per mile, i.e. weight of carriages included."

Major Pangborn had struck exactly the right tone in the way he had edited, used italics to highlight, and arranged a simple account of the work of his grandfather.

Most gratifying was the final sentence that Major Pangborn had crafted, including the emphasis of capital letters to make the point.

> "These facts – taking Smiles' own basis – prove the AUTHOR of the railway system to have been Timothy Hackworth, who was born 22nd December, 1786, at Wylam-on-Tyne, where he introduced the locomotive in 1811."
>
> (COPYRIGHT RESERVED BY J. W. HACKWORTH, DARLINGTON.)

It put Samuel Smiles and the claims he perpetuated in their proper place. And brought Timothy Hackworth to the attention of the world as the man who set the railway on its way. And the whole document was attributed to Uncle John. One way and another, between them, the ranks of the Hackworth family were bringing pioneer Timothy Hackworth the public recognition he deserved.

According to the facts, no one now could dissent from his grandfather's rightful place. The fruits of the sagacity of Mr Hackworth were at long last being acknowledged and applauded. He was the man without whom the locomotive would not have prospered – that was the truth.

CHAPTER TWENTY ONE

All good things have
to come to an end

WORLD'S COLUMBIAN COMMISSION.

OFFICE OF THE

Director-General of the Exposition.

DEPARTMENT
TRANSPORTATION EXHIBITS:
RAILWAYS, VESSELS, VEHICLES.
WILLARD A. SMITH, Chief

Chicago, Ill. U.S.A. Aug.st 30th 93

Dear Cousin Sam,

What a year this has been, for me and for the family. The Expo is drawing to an end soon and grandfather's portrait has been seen by hundreds of thousands of people. I did a rough calculation which Major Pangborn assures me is more right than wrong. Over seven hundred and fifty thousand people of the millions who came to the Expo visited the Transportation Department. Seeing so many every day and talking to them about Timothy Hackworth as one of the pioneers of locomotive transport, it felt like many more!

Major Pangborn is going to write to you shortly about what he plans to do next. If you thought that this Expo had been ambitious you are in for a surprise. The B&O are going to preserve all their exhibits in a new

WORLD'S COLUMBIAN COMMISSION.

OFFICE OF THE

Director-General of the Exposition.

Chicago. Ill. U.S.A. Aug^{st} 30th 93

DEPARTMENT
TRANSPORTATION EXHIBITS:
RAILWAYS, VESSELS, VEHICLES.
WILLARD A. SMITH, Chief

Museum. A local man of business, Marshall Field, has been persuaded to fund it and that Major Pangborn will be one of its directors. He is going to be head of the Commission to travel throughout the world to bring together the most complete set of exhibits of the means of travel ever seen. It will be a National Museum – and unless I am mistaken he will soon turn it into an International Museum. He never does anything by halves. He even managed to get Locomotive 999 to the Expo just after it had broken the 100 miles per hour speed record. So I'm sure he will succeed with this venture too.

He does want your approval for him to hang on to the display, the portrait and the family letters etc that he has. He tells me it will all be stored securely awaiting his return. This could be another stepping stone for the family to keep the work and reputation of grandfather in the public eye well after the Expo has concluded. I think he has in mind that I would help catalogue it all, so we can be sure it will be well looked after.

Do say Yes. I can hardly believe that we have yet another Godsend, even more prestigious than the Expo.

Your Cousin Tim

271

CHAPTER TWENTY TWO

A death in the family

NEW YORK AND PACIFIC STEAMSHIP, COAL AND LUMBER COMPANY.

DIRECT STEAMSHIP LINE
BETWEEN
NEW YORK AND PACIFIC COAST.
MONTHLY SAILINGS.

MORRIS BUILDING,
64, 66 & 68 BROAD STREET.

SAMUEL HOLMES, General Agent.
Cable Address: Holmes, New York.
Watkins & Scott's 10th Edition Codes.
Telephone Call: 1010 Broad.

NEW YORK, 23 July 1894

Dear Cousin Robert,

The worst news possible. Cousin Timothy has passed into God's hands. He went to California hoping that the warmth and sunshine would ease his TB but it was not to be. The funeral is next week and I expect will be well attended.

I have been in contact with his wife Leonor. She is staying in Chicago until the funeral and then coming to stay with her parents in New York. Time enough then to talk with her about managing his affairs.

The legacy he leaves the family is all that he accomplished at the Chicago Exposition. Major Pangborn has plans for it but I now discover he is shortly going away on a tour around the world and not likely to return to America for two years. I am not sure how much he can be relied on to continue to promote grandfather's work as Timothy had done. Perhaps it falls to you and I to try and make as much of grandfather's reputation in England as Timothy accomplished here? However it's done we must follow his lead. Whatever we produce, we must make it readable or the facts will never be learned. It is not the engineering profession we must reach. It is the general public.

Afterword

So last of all...There can be no doubt that without the drive, determination, sheer hard work and effort by George Stephenson the cause of Railways in England, and in the world beyond, would have stumbled. George Stephenson had persisted where others pulled back; had persisted despite the setbacks; had persisted against the establishment; had persisted until he won. The Liverpool & Manchester Railway caught the imagination of businessmen and the population alike, and it put money in the pockets of investors. The person who said 'Let England but make the railways and the railways will be the making of England.' had it right; the social and economic impact of the Industrial Revolution was moved into the fast lane.

The 'Railway mania' that ensued connected centres of trade and commerce across the whole of England – and where there were railways and plans for railways the Stephensons, father and son, were never far away from the action. They didn't miss a trick. They had competed and won at the Rainhill Trials – a competition they had to win to stop the prize of the very railways themselves slipping from their grasp.

It was Timothy Hackworth who built the locomotives that had made that possible; locomotives that stood up to the rigours of their task; locomotives that he continually developed as experience showed the way; locomotives built on technical innovations he readily shared. The person who said 'Timothy Hackworth never made his own fortune, whilst making the fortune of the locomotive' had it right; his solutions to practical problems came from experience, their impact turned the locomotive into a viable proposition for all.

The list of inventions attributable to Timothy Hackworth alone is formidable. 'Simplicity and Economy' were his watchwords – evident in both the blast-pipe and the offset crankshaft. They were key contributions to the design of the 'Planet style locomotives; a design that became the established standard. From the beginning, George Stephenson found it easier to be party to developments with others that led to patentable ideas rather than devise anything of merit himself. Patents with Dodd, in respect of the 'Blucher' locomotive, and with Losh in the metal rails, proved to be of little value as technology developed and raced on. It was a time when claims to ownership – as he'd discovered with Davy and the miner's lamp – could be challenged or avoided. Realising how much of a moving target progress with the locomotive was, he went on to build his success and reputation by cresting the wave of the progress and success of others. He judged the tide in the affairs of man and locomotive well.

Hackworth built locomotives, Stephenson carved out railways. Locomotives hauled goods and carried passengers. Railways charged for hauling goods and carrying passengers for profit. Each man made a pivotal contribution in their field. In the end, Hackworth's work with locomotives led to the building of Shildon, a town that was the centre of the Stockton & Darlington Railway; Stephenson and son's competitive urge, experience, status and connections led them to frame and establish some of the major railways in England. Each is worthy of recognition for their part in our industrial heritage, a pioneering part made possible through meeting the needs and challenges of the Stockton & Darlington Railway.

Hackworth was truly the 'Father of the Locomotive'; George Stephenson was emphatically the 'Father of the Railway' and the Pease family decidedly gave birth to what was without doubt the 'Cradle of the Railway', the Stockton & Darlington Railway. There should be no doubt about the standing of these three men and their railway – it could only have been created through their combined sense of purpose, energies, skill and endeavours – and from which sprang railways that liberated the forces of the Industrial Revolution.

George Stephenson has his time and a place in our heritage. Time now for recognition and the permanent place due to Hackworth. As Smiles would have it 'the true foundation of the railway system was the man who invented such a locomotive as made locomotion practicable and profitable'. The job that Timothy Hackworth Young took on at the Columbian Exposition in Chicago in 1893 is yet to be completed in Hackworth's own country. Pangborn at Baltimore & Ohio had it right too, it is time Timothy

276

Hackworth came out of the shadows to claim his rightful place as the man who at a crucial time "is actually improving the locomotive in essentials as no other man is doing".

Michael Alan Norman, York, 2022

Add your voice to the quest...
Tell all your friends about the book
Post a link to timothyhackworth.com on your social media pages
Thank you

Mike Norman

Bibliography and Sources

Books
The Stephensons
'George & Robert Stephenson: A Passion for Success.'
David Ross 2010 & Nov 2018
'George & Robert Stephenson : The Railway Revolution.'
L T C Rolt 2010 & Jan 2016
'George Stephenson The remarkable life of the founder
of the railways.' Hunter Davies 1975 & 2004
'George Stephenson The engineer and his letters .' W O
Skeat 1973
'The life of George Stephenson and of his son Robert
Stephenson.' Samuel Smiles [1868 8thEdition]

Stockton & Darlington Railway
'The origin of Railway Enterprise: The Stockton and
Darlington Railway 1821-1863.' Maurice W Kirby 1993 &
2010
'Jubilee memorial of the railway system. A history of
the Stockton and Darlington Railway and a record of its
results.' J S Jeans 1875.
'Stockton and Darlington – One Hundred and fifty years
of British Railway.' P W B Semmens 1975
'First in the world – The Stockton and Darlington
Railway.' J Wall 2001

Steam Locomotives

'A history of Railway Locomotives down to the end of the year 1831.' Chapman Frederick Marshall [reprint edition 2011]

'The British Steam Locomotive 1825-1925.' E L Ahrons 1927

'A practical treatise on locomotive engines'– experiments at Liverpool 1834.' F M G Pambour 1836

'Locomotive Engineering and the mechanism of railways.' Zerah Colborn 1871

'Railways in England 1826 and 1827.' Von Oeynhausen & Von Dechen 1971

'A practical treatise on railroads and interior communications in general....' Nicholas Wood 1825

"Evolution of the Steam Locomotive (1803-1898) " G A Sekon 1899

Digitised by Google University of California Berkeley Libraries

archive.org Google 'evolutionofsteam00nokerich'

Rainhill Trials

'The Rainhill Trials.' Christopher McGowan 2004

'The Rainhill Story. Anthony Burton 1980

Science Museum: The Rainhill Trials October 1829 inc Robert Stephenson's five letters to Henry Booth, timetable for construction of Rocket etc

NRM :1829 Rastrick Notebook – Rainhill Run times & Comments

Carey Collection : Miscellaneous Pamphlets by Mathew Carey – Collected April 1831

p438 Essay on Railways p444-462 London Mechanics

Magazine reprint for Oct 10 1829 [Rainhill] Oct 17
1829 etc Extensive account of Rainhill and detail of the
locomotives. Haithi Trust
Original : University of Michigan Transportation
Library H33 C27
Presented to Samuel Richard Esq as a mark of respect &
esteem

Carey & Lea Collection : 5 reports Published 1831, Philadelphia 227pg

'Report to the directors of the Liverpool and Manchester
Railway on the comparative merits of Locomotive and
Fixed Engines as a moving power.' James Walker March
1829
'Observations on the comparative merits of Locomotive
and Fixed Engines as applied to Railways.' Robert
Stephenson and Joseph Locke
'An Account of the competition of locomotive engines
Rainhill October 1829.'
'An Account of the Liverpool and Manchester Railway.'
Henry Booth, Treasurer to the Company [5 Chapters,
Appendix and Observations to December 15 1830]
Digitised by Google – archive.org>details>reporttodirect
000bootgoug
Original : Donated Jul 31 1914 John B Thayer to Harvard
College Eng 835.31

General

Arcana of Science and Art 1830
Marked : Per 379 1991 e. 100/1830 Digitised by Google
– archive.org

Imperial Cyclopaedia of Machinery– William Johnson
1854
Dedicated to Napier. Haithi Trust
Marked : University of California M130270

Timothy Hackworth

'Timothy Hackworth and the Locomotive.' R Young 1923,
1975 & 2000
Memoir – Timothy Hackworth - November 1892
Unpublished Foreword by Samuel Holmes to 'Timothy
Hackworth and the Locomotive' by Robert Young

Pangborn

'Picturesque on the B&O.' J G Pangborn 1884 Haithi
Trust
Library of Congress Digitised by Internet Archive
Copyright C K Lord
'The world's rail way, historical, descriptive, illustrative;'
J G Pangborn 1896
*University of California Digitised by Google archive.
org/details/worldsrailwayhis00pangrich*
[Reprint as The golden age of the steam locomotive 2003
Dover Publications]

Exposition – Various historic records

'The World's Columbian Exposition Chicago 1893.' 658p
Haithi Trust
Many other reports and catalogs for the Exposition

Paul V Galvin Library Comprehensive account of the
Exposition
Columbus.lit.edu

World's Columbian Exposition (1893: Chicago)
*https://onlinebooks.library.upenn.edu/webbin/book/
lookupname?key=World%27s%20Columbian%20
Exposition%20%281893%20%3A%20Chicago%2C%20
Ill%2E%29* Extensive catalog of papers/reports for the
Expo

Journals

I am indebted to Haithi Trust for various historic copies
of Practical Mechanics Journal and to archive.org for
various historic copies of Mechanics Magazine.

Sources : Chapter by Chapter

Chapter 7

'The battle of life..'
    Smiles: Self Help 1859 Ch XI p171 of 205
'my father, having observed...'
    Smiles :Life of George Stephenson Ch V p168
'It was only when...' '..sagacity of Timothy Hackworth'
    Smiles : Life of George Stephenson Ch V p173
'We have tried the new locomotive engine at Bolton,...'
    NRM : George Stephenson to Timothy Hackworth
    HACK/1/1/11
    Described as 'the blast pipe' letter. Dated 28 July
    1828

Chapter 8

*News of Chicago Milwaukee Union Ticket Office at
Exposition*
    Chicago Daily News Almanac 1893 p199

Chapter 10

'This engine, when altered, was known as the 'Royal George' and commenced...'

Locomotive Engineering and The Mechanism of Railways 1871

Colborn : Description of 'Royal George' p21

'The history of the Steam-Engine offers to our notice a series of contrivances...'

The Imperial Cyclopaedia of Machinery : Stationary, Marine and Locomotive Engines 1854 : Dr Dionysus Lardner p17

'She was named the 'Royal George, and commenced working in October, 1827'

The Imperial Cyclopaedia of Machinery 1854

Dr Dionysus Lardner : Account of locomotives superiority p74

'The points of improvement in the "Royal George" which conduced to this...

The Imperial Cyclopaedia of Machinery 1854

Dr Dionysus Lardner : Improvements and Invention of blast pipe p74

'Up to the period of which we write, no really efficient locomotive was in use..'

The Imperial Cyclopaedia of Machinery 1854

Dr Dionysus Lardner : Power of blast pipe p74

Chapter 11

'I say he never had a plan – I believe he never had one – I do not believe he is capable of making one'

Edward Alderson – leading counsel : Hansard May 31 1825

Chapter 12

Robert Stephenson riposte in favour of the locomotive
Carey & Lea p111

'Where the trade is great and nearly uniform..'
Robert Stephenson : Stationery & Locomotive equal
Carey & Lea p119

'The reports of the Engineers who visited the North...'
NRM :Robert Stephenson to Timothy Hackworth.
HACK/ 1/1 /21
Requests his view and information

'My general opinion, as to the L M System. I believe it is in a comparative...'
NRM : Timothy Hackworth to Robert Stephenson.
HACK/1/1/22
Locomotives not Stationary Engines and Load to be carried

'...to enable you to take advantage of the improvements...'
Rastrick and Walker – propose premium for best design Carey & Lea p51

Chapter 13

'The true history of the thing is this:- I was driver of the 'Royal George'...
Gowland's letter on superiority of Royal George:
Engineer 23/10/57 p304
'William Gowland: Days worked 269..'
M W Kirby : The origins of Railway enterprise...1993 p66
1828 Drivers records – 25 % more Load carried
"Royal George" had the blast pipe; and not only so, but, to make a certainty...

NRM: 12/1/1876 – JWH to Engineer Northern Echo
HACK/3/1/33
Multiple use of exhausted steam in Royal George

Chapter 14

Notebook of John Urpeth Rastrick
NRM Archive *'RAST' :* Rainhill Locomotives and Trial
times
Also reported in Canadian Rail No489 2002 p127-130
*'Sanspareil, after allowing for its greater weight, was
the most powerful engine.'*
Locomotive Engineering and The Mechanism of
Railways 1871
Colborn: failure not attributable to any defect in the
principle. p29

Chapter 15

'Indeed the feeling at the moment was very prevalent,...'
Booth : Erroneous notion of going over Inclines Carey
& Lea p207
*Experiment First, Experiment Second 'In confirmation
of these...'*
Robert Stephenson : Experiments with Load after
Rainhil Carey & Lea p89
*'On the 14ᵗʰ of the present month, (June,) an experiment
was made..'*
Booth: Run for Directors with improved Rocket type
Carey & Lea p225
*'The gross weight drawn was about 33 tons, consisting
as follows:-'*
Booth : assistant locomotive & speed dropped to
4mph Carey & Lea p226

Chapter 16

*'In one of my father's memorandum books I find he
started on a journey...'*

NRM: John Wesley Hackworth – response to Gray
HACK/3/1/16
30 March 1852 :Progress, or lack of, at RS&Co, with
Globe and Planet

*'Taking this performance as a fair criterion, which there
is no reason to doubt..'*

Booth : Planet drawing load of goods with assistance
Carey & Lea p227

Chapter 17

*'applied to engines but two or three years from the
maker's workshops,..'*

Locomotive Engineering and The Mechanism of
Railways 1871
Colborn : L&MR Defects and cost of repairs p37

'it is necessary to mention what is meant by repairs...'

Pambour: 1834 A treatise on locomotive engines p538
Repair, reconstruction, rebuild

'We have said elsewhere...'

Pambour: 1836 A practical treatise on locomotive
engines upon railway in form and construction p333
Liverpool & Manchester Railway Costly repairs and
locomotives set aside

'We cannot proceed...'

NRM: Nov 8 1831 – H Dickinson to Timothy
Hackworth, HACK/3/3/1/2
Napier patent letter from RS&Co, design violates
Napier patent

*"Hackworth immediately got in communication with
Robert Napier...'*
JWH handwritten note: Response and record of visit

Chapter 18

*'The Liverpool and Manchester Railway, in reference
to the formation of the road, and to all the moving
machinery,is yet far from completed. From the opening
of the Railway to the present time, and, more especially,
for the past 12 or 18 months we have been in a state of
transition, passing from the defective and imperfect, in
form and construction, to more improved forms, and
especially to increased strength in engines, coaches and
wagons.'*

*'gradually these defects are in course of being remedied,
but time and money are indispensable in this process,
and the work of transition from wrong to right is far
from being accomplished; further time will be needed,
and further sums must be expended.'*
Irish Railway Commission 1838: H Booth Evidence 1836
Appendix A No9 p77
*'The Stockton and Darlington Railway being the first
of its kind (for public use and general traffic) cannot
be taken as the best specimen; though I am not certain,
as to its repair, management, and efficiency, or even
public utility, that the Directors need yield the palm to
any other party.'*
Irish Railway Commission 1838 : J Pease Evidence 1836
Appendix A No11 p87

Chapter 20

'Hackworth's engine with 11–inch cylinders and a 20-inch stroke...'
> Locomotive Engineering and The Mechanism of Railways 1871
> Colborn: Hackworth thus led the way in the proportions ...p25

'The FIRST public railway was the Stockton & Darlington, opened September 27th,'
> NRM : John Wesley Hackworth (WYLAM) to papers. HACK/3/1/46
> Daily Chronicle September 29 1885 – history, blast pipe, economics

Chapter 21

Announcement in New York Times of Pangborn's departure: Sept 23 1894
> Pangborn's two year trip – for Marshall Field Museum

Note:

Carey & Lea Collection – page numbers refer to the absolute number in the report overall, not the page numbers in the individual reports it contains.

Colborn – page numbers are actual page numbers of the book

Smiles – the 8th edition was the last, but the first in which Hackworth was given credit compared with the disparaging remarks in footnotes and content attributable to Robert Stephenson in earlier editions. It was also after Robert Stephenson's extensive notes, to Smiles in 1857, shortly before his early death.

Glossary of Characters

Narrators and the Family

John Wesley Hackworth : Eldest son of Timothy Hackworth. Worked alongside his father. Delivered a locomotive in Russia to the Tsar when aged 16. Devised and patented his 'Hackworth valve gear'. Repeatedly sought to resist claims by other people to have invented the 'blast pipe' and to make clear his father's contribution to locomotive development.

Timothy Hackworth : Stepped into his father's shoes at an early age. Served his apprenticeship and became headsmith at Wylam Colliery at age 24. Remained there developing locomotives until his Methodist principles forced him to move away to Walbottle colliery. Subsequently was approached by George Stephenson to join him – firstly supervising the building of his locomotives for the Stockton and Darlington Railway, then to take on the job of Superintendent for the railway company itself. He remained with the company for fifteen years, during which time he devised different forms of locomotive and ensured the railway's successful expansion.

Samuel Holmes : Grandson of Timothy Hackworth. Emigrated to America and established a shipping agency in New York. Spent early childhood living with the Hackworth family.

Prudence Nightingale : Matriach of the Hackworth family at the time of the Exposition. Married to Charles Nightingale, Methodist Minister.

Major Pangborn : Appointed by the founder of the Baltimore and Ohio Railroad Company to promote the all important passenger traffic. Visited Europe and collected an extensive account of early locomotive development in preparation for the Chicago World's Fair.

Robert Young : Grandson of Timothy Hackworth, cousin to Sam Holmes and Timothy Young. Emigrated to Penang.

Timothy Hackworth Young : Grandson of Timothy Hackworth. Joined his cousin in New York before moving to Chicago, working as a Foreman for the Chicago, Milwaukee, St. Paul and Pacific Railroad – known as the "Milwaukee Road" line.

Thomas Hackworth : Younger brother of Timothy Hackworth who followed in his footsteps from Wylam to Walbottle and would manage the workshops set up in Shildon. He later went on to establish an engineering company that would become noted for marine engines.

The Railway Men

Henry Booth : Secretary to the Liverpool and Manchester Railway, instigator and co-designer of 'Rocket', the locomotive with a multi-tube boiler.

Edward Pease : Prime mover and co-founder of the Stockton & Darlington Railway. Partner with the Stephensons in the locomotive works.

Joseph Pease : Son of founder Edward Pease, he took responsibility for the Stockton and Darlington Railway when his father stepped down in 1829.

George Stephenson : The man who put the stamp of the steam locomotive on the spread of the railways. Firstly for the transport of coal from mines, then of passengers on railways that linked commercial centres.

Robert Stephenson : Son of George Stephenson. Educated at Edinburgh University, and as apprentice to Nicholas Wood at Killingworth. Took three year assignment in S America. Returned to the role of constructor of 'Rocket', locomotives for the Manchester and Liverpool Railway, surveyor of railways, engineer of bridges. Promoted the cause of his father with Samuel Smiles.

Main players

Zerah Colburn : Engineer, author of a book on the principles and construction of the locomotive engine.

William Gowland : Locomotive driver for Timothy Hackworth of 'Royal George'

Charles Lord : Vice President of the Baltimore & Ohio Railroad Company.

Francouis Pambour : French engineer who conducted experiments at Manchester and Liverpool line looking to develop a theory of locomotive design.

John Rastrick : Engineer, locomotive designer, co-author of report for directors of Liverpool & Manchester Railway, judge at the Rainhill Trials.

Marc Seguin : French locomotive engineer and designer of a 'multi-tube boiler'.

Samuel Smiles : Biographer of George Stephenson.

Incidental characters – Extras

John Braithwaite : Co-designer with John **Ericson** of locomotive 'Novelty' that competed at Rainhill.

Edward Bury : Locomotive builder, challenger to Stephensons for supply to the Liverpool and Manchester Railway.

George Davidson : Locomotive driver of 'Samson', Hackworth's locomotive for the Albany Mines at Pictou in Canada.

Ralph Dodds : Manager of Killingworth mine when George Stephenson was a young man, joint patent holder with George Stephenson of locomotive design.

John Garrett : President and instigator of the Baltimore and Ohio Railroad Company.

Goldsworthy Gurney : Designer of steam engine for use on roads.

Richard Harrison : Director of Liverpool and Manchester Railway, instigator of the locomotive competition and the Rainhill Trials.

William Hedley : Manager of Wylam mine, insisted on the men working on Sunday.

Dr Dyonisus Lardner : Academic and commentator on the steam locomotive.

Frederick Layton : Director of the 'Milwaukee Road' railroad. (An Englishman).

Michael Longridge : Owner of local iron works, partner in locomotive works.

William Losh : Iron founder and, with George Stephenson, joint holder of patent for iron rails for railway track.

Robert Morrow : Locomotive driver for Timothy Hackworth.

George Overton : Surveyor of original line for Stockton & Darlington.

William Patter : Employed Timothy Hackworth as foreman smith at Walbottle.

Thomas Telford : Eminent engineer, called on to inspect and evaluate Stephenson's construction of the Manchester to Liverpool railroad.

James Walker : Engineer, co-author of report for directors of Liverpool & Manchester Railway.

James Watt : Inventor of the steam engine.

Nicholas Wood : Manager of Killingworth mine, author of 'A practical treatise on railroads and interior communications in general....', judge at Rainhill Trials.

Early English pioneers : Richard Trevithick, John Blenkinsop, William Hedley.

The American pioneers : Mathew Baldwin, Ross Winans, Horatio Allen.

Walk on Parts

William Tranton : Imaginary name for Foreman at Baltimore & Ohio Roundhouse, refered to in Timothy Young's letter to Aunt Prudence, who showed him the exhibits.

Brigham : Imagined character – Assistant to Major Pangborn.

Sanspareil : Hackworth's locomotive was named from the French for 'without equal', and its name was recorded as one word 'Sanspareil' in early documents/ reports. However, in more recent times it often appears as the two separate words 'Sans' 'Pareil'.